D1106097

FLICKERTAIL STORIES
of times ever gone

by

Erling Nicolai Rolfsrud

LANTERN BOOKS

Farwell, Minnesota 56327

FLICKERTAIL STORIES
of times ever gone

First Printing, September, 1989

ISBN 0-914689-13-4

Printed in the United States of America
by
Echo Printing
Alexandria, Minnesota 56308

Dedicated

to the boys and girls

of North Dakota

Contents

Yellow Blossom's Wedding 1
Bird Woman 7
White Indian 12
Cart Boy 23
Lord Milton Rides The Red 28
Crane Hunt 32
Mystery Hole 37
Exit Uncle Buffalo 40
The Professor's Palace Car 48
Hunter's Paradise 52
Wind Wagons 58
Wheat-Cleaner 61
Overcomer 64
Sodbusting Sisters 67
To See A Tree 71
Where Is Crary? 75
Plank-Rider 78
Gas Buggies 81
The Rampaging Mouse 90
Sculptor 95
Cookcar Girl 97
Nurse Boy 109
"Tree-Tops" 113

Foreword

This book tells of people doing what none of us will ever do. It tells of times and places ever gone. It offers bits of history not recorded in history books.

In *Flickertail Stories,* you will read about ordinary people. But they all showed spunk. Oldtimers used that word often, though we seldom hear it today. Spunk means pluck, courage, a spirit of overcoming.

In these pages you will meet some spunky individuals. An eleven-year-old boy nurses his family of eleven persons, all ill with the dread Spanish Influenza rampant during World War I. Not having money to buy an automobile, a sixteen-year-old boy builds his own gas buggy. A fourteen-year-old boy holds fast to a plank high above the Missouri River. A young mother guards her small children while a wolf stalks about her muslin tent. Women turn the sod and build a dwelling of their own. A hunter's bride sews clothes from skins by tallow light in a buffalo-skin-covered dugout.

Spunk does not always bring the winning of a goal. Captured by Indians in 1789, nine-year-old John Tanner lived a life of courage. Young George Northrop set out with handcart and dog to walk across the western wilderness in 1855. Neither of these boys succeeded in what he set out to do. Yet they leave us a legacy of pluck that stirs our hearts.

Adversity, not ease and comfort, nurtures the overcoming spirit. As Francis Bacon wrote five hundred years ago, "He knows not his own strength that hath not met adversity." Today, as in years past, people can use hardships and obstacles as challenges, or use them as causes for complaints.

1 - Hidatsa Indian maiden. Painting by George Catlin, 1832.

1 - *Yellow Blossom's Wedding*

The hollow buffalo hooves at the earth-lodge doorway clitter-clattered. Yellow Blossom and her family turned to see Cowbird enter.

The old Hidatsa Indian walked quietly toward the fire in the center of the earth-lodge. There Yellow Blossom's father, Strong Wolf, sat warming himself. Cowbird respectfully placed his right hand upon Strong Wolf's head and said: "You know that we have in our family a good son, a great hunter, and we want him to live in your family. We ask that you do us this good favor, for it would please our Hunts-Eagle and our family to have your Yellow Blossom for his wife."

Yellow Blossom could hardly believe what she was hearing. All her life she had known that when she grew up, when she had learned all the skills of an earth-lodge wife, she would marry. She had sometimes seen this Hunts-Eagle dancing with other painted young men as they told of their great hunting deeds.

Now she quietly listened as Cowbird walked over to her two mothers, Corn Tassel and Red Feather, and spoke the same words to each of them. This done, he left the earth-lodge.

It seemed a very long time before either her father or her mothers spoke. Yellow Blossom waited silently. Whatever Strong Wolf decided, that she must obey.

Finally, Strong Wolf turned from the fire and said to his two wives, "I think not that my daughter is ready to marry. Does she yet know all that would make her a good wife?"

Corn Tassel smiled. "Yellow Blossom has learned well how to cook. She can dress skins. She sews with the awl and sinew. She made the moccasins you wear. She has made clothing and tent covers."

And Red Feather added, "She has digged our corn fields, and she sings beautifully the songs to help the corn grow. She has harvested and dried our squash for winter. And because she has never been lazy but always ready to work and do her part, her clan aunt, Gooseberry, made for her the women's belt she wears."

Strong Wolf smiled at Yellow Blossom as she fingered the broad quill-embroidered belt about her waist. That belt was an honor to wear, one that could be given only by a person not a blood relative. It was something to wear as proudly as a young brave the scalp of an enemy.

For answer, Strong Wolf only gazed long into the fire. And as Yellow Blossom went on with her embroidering a moccasin with gull quills, her thoughts jumbled together. Hunts-Eagle was tall and he was handsome. He had gone on several raiding parties against the Sioux and brought back horses stolen from the Hidatsa—and he had taken from the Sioux a buffalo horse. To own horses made a young brave a rich person in the eyes of Hidatsa people.

The more Yellow Blossom thought about Hunts-Eagle, the more she hoped her father would agree to Cowbird's wish. She could think of other young braves she would not want for a husband.

The time passed slowly while Strong Wolf remained silent. Then the buffalo-hoof bells at the door clitter-clattered again. Cowbird stood in the doorway. "Come," he said to Strong Wolf.

Strong Wolf followed outside. Behind him came the two mothers, then Yellow Blossom and her four younger sisters.

Cowbird motioned toward the stage where corn hung to dry. Tied to the stage were three horses and on the backs of each horse, a beautiful buffalo robe. Three of Hunts-Eagle's relatives stood nearby.

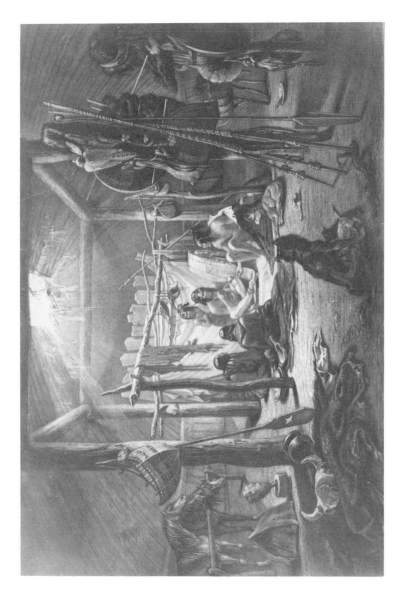

2 - Interior of an earth lodge. Painting by Karl Bodmer.

"See," said Cowbird, "we have brought you three horses and three robes for Yellow Blossom."

Strong Wolf looked slowly at the offered horses, then said, "No. I cannot accept your gifts. I do not believe my daughter is ready to marry yet."

Cowbird and his relatives left, leaving the horses behind. Strong Wolf called to two young men of his clan and asked that they return the horses to Cowbird's lodge.

Yellow Blossom went back to her embroidery, trying hard not to show her disappointment. For the more she had thought about Hunts-Eagle, the more she liked the idea of having him come to her lodge to live. But she must abide by whatever Strong Wolf willed.

Early the next morning, the buffalo hooves clitter-clattered again as Cowbird entered. Once more he asked Strong Wolf to come outside. And again the women followed after. Yellow Blossom's hopes renewed as she saw that now beside the three horses and three robes, a fourth horse, a buffalo-hunting horse had been added. An earth-lodge family that had a horse fleet enough to catch a buffalo could be sure of enough meat.

Saying no more, Cowbird and his relatives left.

Strong Wolf looked carefully at the hunting horse. Then he went back into the lodge.

Again he sat down beside the fire. Often he would glance toward Yellow Blossom as she sewed together a new dress of deerskin for her little half-sister, White Star.

After what seemed a very long time to Yellow Blossom, Strong Wolf stood up and said to his wives, "I know this Hunts-Eagle. He is a good man. He is gentle. He must have his heart set to have Yellow Blossom for wife, or his family would not send us a buffalo horse. So I shall agree and Hunts-Eagle may come to our lodge to live with Yellow Blossom."

Then Strong Wolf turned to Yellow Blossom and said, "My daughter, I want you to take Hunts-Eagle for your husband. Be a good wife to him. Try always to make him happy. Cook food for him, sew his clothes and care for him if he is ever sick or wounded."

Yellow Blossom smiled shyly at her father, happy that Hunts-Eagle would be her husband and not some brave she did not like. All her life she had learned to obey her father and now again she was glad to do so.

For the next days, Strong Wolf helped his two wives to prepare the wedding feast. When all was cooked and ready, the family fastened the pots of steaming hot food to poles so they could be carried on the shoulders of women relatives. Just before all was ready for the march to Cowbird's lodge, Strong Wolf gave Yellow Blossom a muskrat cap decorated with weasel tails. "You give this to Cowbird," he said.

Timidly Yellow Blossom led the wedding procession with her sister, Red Bird, walking beside her. The relatives followed with the food and with Strong Wolf's two horses carrying a beautiful embroidered robe and a many-feathered headdress.

At Cowbird's lodge, Yellow Blossom lifted the skin door and shyly entered. She saw Cowbird sitting on his couch before the fire. She walked to him and placed the muskrat cap upon his head.

Almost trembling at the sight of Hunts-Eagle, she now sat down on the floor near him. Red Bird sat down beside her. But neither said a word to the smiling Hunts-Eagle.

By this time Yellow Blossom's women relatives had set the kettles of food beside the fire, and the men had tied the two horses to the stage outside. They brought in the embroidered robe and the headdress and laid these beside Cowbird. Cowbird accepted them and Yellow Blossom knew that she would truly become Hunts-Eagle's bride.

Now the mother of Hunts-Eagle brought a bowl of buffalo meat for Yellow Blossom and her sister. The two ate quietly and when they had finished, they went home.

Later that day all of Hunts-Eagle's family and relatives came to feast on the food brought from Strong Wolf's lodge. Each of these wedding guests brought with them a gift that the new bride would find useful. That same evening two of Cowbird's wives brought the presents to Strong Wolf's lodge.

Instead of giving the presents directly to Yellow Blossom, they placed them on the floor before her birth mother, Corn Tassel.

During the next days, Corn Tassel helped Yellow Blossom make a new couch and hang tent skins about it. And for Hunts-Eagle, they made a willow chair in which he could sit in front of the enclosed couch.

All this completed, Corn Tassel told her daughter, "Yellow Blossom, now it is time to bring your husband to our lodge. Just go to his father's lodge and sit beside Hunts-Eagle and tell him you want him to come to his new home in your father's lodge."

Almost quivering with excitement, Yellow Blossom called to Red Bird to come with her. The two sisters walked slowly to the lodge of Cowbird. As Yellow Blossom lifted the skin door, she found that not only were all the members of Hunts-Eagle's family there but several other relatives as well. They hushed their talking as Yellow Blossom and Red Bird entered. No one said a word to the two sisters as they crossed the room to where Hunts-Eagle sat on his couch.

Yellow Blossom and Red Bird sat down beside Hunts-Eagle.

Hunts-Eagle smiled at Yellow Blossom.

"I have come for you, my husband," said Yellow Blossom.

"Ah, that is good, my Yellow Blossom," answered Hunts-Eagle.

But he did not stand up from the couch when the two sisters arose and quietly left the lodge.

Slowly and with dignity, Yellow Blossom and Red Bird started back to their own lodge. They knew that Hunts-Eagle would follow a proper distance behind them, and the buffalo hooves in Strong Wolf's doorway would clitter-clatter as the bridegroom entered.

And thus Yellow Blossom and Hunts-Eagle were married.

2 - Bird Woman

"Sakakawea. Sakakawea," the Hidatsa woman repeated again and again to the Shoshone girl captive. Twelve years old and not understanding the Hidatsa tongue, the girl could only look fearfully at the woman who stood over her.

Now pointing close to the frightened girl, the woman said the word over and over, "Sakakawea. Sakakawea. Sakakawea." And somehow, the girl realized this was her new name, her Hidatsa name, here in this strange earth-lodge village on the Knife River.

The days went slowly by as Sakakawea learned to work in the small fields of corn and squash, and to do whatever chore the woman motioned her to do. Little by little, she began to understand some of the woman's words and those of others of the family that lived in the earth lodge. And she came to know that *Sakakawea* meant "Bird Woman."

One day she saw a strange man of white skin and he wore clothes such as Sakakawea had never seen before—clothes of soft woven cloth instead of skin. When other white men came among the Hidatsa, this man spoke a second language. And he helped the visiting white men to barter for furs in exchange for shining beads and bright cloths. And for firewater that made the Indian hunters act badly.

Sakakawea learned the man had a name not of the Hidatsa tongue, but of that second language. Toussaint Charbonneau, he was. Then one day he came to Sakakawea's lodge with many beads and bright cloth, and the Hidatsa family sold Sakakawea to Toussaint Charbonneau to be his slave. The white man took her to the lodge where he lived with his two Indian wives. Not long after, he made Sakakawea his third wife.

When the autumn winds had shaken the leaves off the trees, there came up Grandmother River* a large keelboat and two small boats carrying many white men. They built a fort east of Grandmother River not far from the earthlodge village of the Mandan tribe. Toussaint Charbonneau took his three wives to the white men's fort to live because he had been hired as interpreter.

Sakakawea stared in amazement when she saw that one of the men had red hair, and another one had black skin. She learned that two of the men were like chiefs. One was the red-haired man, Captain William Clark, and the other, Captain Meriweather Lewis. And she learned of the Great White Father who lived far away at a place called Washington, and that he and these white men wanted the Mandan and the Hidatsa and the Arikara earthlodge people to live together in peace. The earthlodge people were few in number and their fierce enemy, the Sioux, were many. So the red-haired man, Captain William Clark, said the earthlodge people should unite against the Sioux. The earthlodge chiefs agreed, saying the Chief Redhead spoke truth with a straight tongue.

Sakakawea tried eagerly to please the white men and Captain Redhead learned how she had been captured, and that she would like to see her own people again. Did she know the way back to the western mountains and to her people? Yes, she did. Then, said Captain Redhead, when spring came, she could go with the white men and show them the way to the Shoshone people. The Shoshone had horses the white men needed for the journey over the montains to the Great Shining Waters of the Pacific Ocean.

---

*Missouri River

That winter Sakakawea gave birth to a boy and Toussaint Charbonneau named him Baptiste. And the white men made six dugout canoes ready for spring when the river would thaw. Early in April the large keelboat was sent down the river to return to St. Louis. The remaining thirty-three men started westward up Grandmother River in their heavily-loaded dugout canoes. And Sakakawea rejoiced that she would see her people again.

No unfriendly Indians troubled them. But grizzly bears several times frightened the men. Rattlesnakes gave them some scary moments as well.

Gentle Sakakawea, carrying her baby on her back, also carried with her a "rattlesnake weed" from which she made a poultice for treating a snake bite. She found sunflower seeds and roots and berries to eat, and she gathered herbs to treat anyone who became sick. She made ointments to heal sores and insect bites.

When a sudden windstorm upset the boat carrying the two captains' papers, medicines, instruments and maps, Sakakawea jumped into the water and saved them. And at last in mid August, she sighted an encampment of Shoshone people. Great was Sakakawea's joy to discover that the chief was her own brother Cameahwait. She gave him a lump of sugar she had saved and promised him that if his people would be friends with the white men, he would get more sugar. Later, Sakakawea helped get the Shoshone to trade horses to the white men and also to furnish a guide across the Mountains of Bright Stones to where a river flowed west to the Great Shining Waters.

After crossing the Bitter Root Mountains and reaching the Clearwater River, the expedition left their horses with the Nez Perce Indians. They then went down river in dugout canoes and built themselves a fort not far from the ocean. Here they spent the winter.

A great day it was for Sakakawea when the white captains took her to see the ocean. There she stared in astonishment at a whale that had washed ashore.

3 - Statue of Sakakawea on capitol grounds, Bismarck

The following spring the expedition started back and after many adventures reached the place where their Fort Mandan had been. A prairie fire had burned it to the ground. But warm welcome awaited the white men in the Mandan earthlodge villages.

The two captains paid Toussaint Charbonneau five hundred dollars for his services as interpreter. Sakakawea received nothing and expected nothing. Yet she had been one of the most valuable members of the Lewis and Clark Expedition; she had not only guided the white men to the Shoshones and helped get horses for them, she had also helped those who became ill and found extra food along the way.

The expedition left Sakakawea and her husband at the Mandan villages and went back to the Great White Father at Washington.

It is believed that Sakakawea died at Fort Manuel Lisa on December 20, 1812, after giving birth to a little girl. Later her son and daughter were both adopted and cared for by Captain Clark.

On the Capitol grounds at Bismarck stands a statue of Sakakawea. Sponsored by the North Dakota Federation of Women's Clubs and sculptured by Leonard Crunelle, it was presented to the state in October, 1910. North Dakota school children gave their pennies to help finance the cost of the statue.

The Garrison Dam across the Missouri holds back a great reservoir of water. That reservoir is named Lake Sakakawea in honor of the gentle Bird Woman.

3 - White Indian

Nine-year-old John Tanner was angry. Here he must stay in the house, taking care of his baby brother while his father and older brother worked in the field. John decided that one way or another, he would get out of this house that had been shuttered and barred against Indians.

So he pinched the baby until it cried and his stepmother took it from him to nurse. And while she was busy, John managed to steal out. Then he slipped out of the fortified yard through a small door, leaving it open behind him.

He dashed for a walnut tree and began hunting for nuts. He had dropped only a few nuts into his hat when he heard a crackling behind him. He turned and saw two Indians close by and watching him. Before John could cry out for his father, the older Indian clapped his hand over John's mouth and dragged him away. And so that spring of 1789 out in the Kentucky wilderness, young John was kidnapped and he would never again take care of his infant brother.

(This happened at a time when white men were pushing westward into the American wilderness, killing Indians so they could turn Indian hunting grounds into farms. Likewise, the Indians were killing whites as they tried to keep what had been theirs for centuries past. Both whites and Indians fought savagely.)

Now as the Indians dragged John through the woods, he fainted. The next he knew, he lay at the edge of a river where several Indians were getting into a hickory-bark canoe. One of his captors raised a hatchet over John's head, but the younger Indian who had helped kidnap him knocked the hatchet aside and so saved John's life.

Then they tossed John into the canoe and paddled a short distance down the Ohio River. They crossed to the opposite shore. Here they pulled from a hollow tree some blankets and food they had hidden inside it. They saw the corn field where John's father and brother were working, and the Indians laughed as they pointed to them.

For days afterward, the Indians hurried further into the wilderness. They took John's shoes away from him, thinking he could run faster barefooted. Each night, exhausted, the boy fell quickly asleep under a blanket between the two Indians that had captured him. Finally, when John's feet were bleeding and bruised, the older man pulled out thorns and gave John an old pair of moccasins. By this time, John had learned the older man was named Manito-o-geezik and he was the father of Kish-kau-ko who had saved John's life.

They stopped at a Shawnee Indian village where Indians who hated the sight of any white person tried to kill John, but always the old man and Kish-kau-ko protected him. They paused for a while at a white man's fortified trading post where white men tried to buy John from the Indians, but the old man would not sell. And while John had thus far tried to believe he would somehow escape and had kept cheerful, now he gave up hope and cried.

In a canoe John's captors followed along the western shore of Lake Erie until they came to Detroit which was then a well-fortified trading post. French-Canadians had small farms and fields near by.

John's heart leaped with hope when his captors drew near the shore and talked to a white woman there. But the woman spoke in a language John could not understand. A short while later, after they had paddled a good distance beyond the fort, the

Indians took John into some woods, put him in a hollow log and fixed it so he could not get out.

The next morning the Indians returned with three horses, and with some of them riding, others running slongside, they three days later reached the Shawnee village of Saginaw. Here Manito-o-geezik had his lodge and out of it came a woman. When the old man spoke to her, she immediately began crying, then hugging and kissing John.

Then they took the white boy to where the old woman's son had been buried. Here they danced and sang and gave strings of beads and birch-bark boxes filled with maple sugar and corn to John -- but just as quickly they took the gifts away from him.

When John lay down to sleep that night, he realized that he had been kidnapped so that he could take the place of the Indian boy who had died.

And he could tell that his Indian family had given him a strange-sounding name: Shaw-shaw-wa ne-ba-se. One day he would learn that it meant "The Falcon."

* * * * * * * *

Life with his Shawnee family became a mixture of kindness and cruelty. Manito-o-geezik, the father, considered him a child of the hated whites and beat him regularly, and John was made to labor with the women. But in the fall, he went with the hunters and helped build corrals in which to trap deer. Little by little he learned Shawnee words.

Then one day after hours of working in the cornfield, John fell asleep at his work. Manito-o-geezik found him and hit John on the head with his tomahawk. He tossed the unconscious boy into the bushes, then found his wife and told her, "The boy I brought you is good for nothing, so I have killed him."

John, however, had only been knocked senseless. When he revived, he found his Indian mother and her daughter crying bitterly and pouring cold water over his bruised head.

And so John learned never to fall asleep at work and that his best friends among the Shawnee Indians were the women.

Often when the old father did not allow John to eat, the mother stole a little food and hid it for John until Manito-o-geezik was gone.

After a miserable winter of cold and hunger and many beatings from Manito-o-geezik, the time came for tapping the maple trees for sap, and John worked hard with the women. When the maple sap had been made into sugar, the father and his son Kish-kau-ko and four other warriors set out for the Kentucky settlements. "I am going there to kill your family," Manito-o-geezik told John.

Weeks later, the father returned with a hat and when John examined the hat, he found his brother Edward's initials inside it. Believing that his entire family had been killed as Manito-o-geezik boasted, John gave up hope of ever returning to Kentucky. Furthermore, Manito-o-geezik boasted that the Indians were beating back all the white settlers.

And so John realized he could no longer think of himself as John Tanner, a white boy, but he must learn to live like an Indian and become The Falcon.

One day there came to the lodge of Manito-o-geezik a woman chief of the the Ottawa tribe. Not long before, her son, the age of John, had died. Now she, Net-nok-wa, had come to buy this white boy captive she had heard about; the white boy would take the place of her dead son. The Shawnee mother wept in despair, for she did not want to give up her Falcon.

But Netnokwa had brought gifts, and among these a ten-gallon keg of whiskey. With Manito-o-geezik drunk and laden with gifts, the bargain was struck. Netnokwa (who never drank) took the white boy by the hand and led him to her own lodge. Here she gave him new clothes and said, "Now you are my son!"

John soon learned that while Netnokwa was Ottawa, her husband was a young Chippewa. Though Netnokwa was a woman, she was a chief among the Ottawa. And in her lodge, she, not her husband, was in charge and she owned everything in her lodge. Afraid that white traders would take her white son from her, Netnokwa now decided they should go west into her husband's Chippewa country.

John's new father treated him kindly. He never hit John and he called him his son. But Netnokwa, being the head of the family, ordered that her white son must do woman's work. However, she always dealt gently with him.

John yearned to become a hunter, for now he knew that among the Indians a boy must prove himself a good hunter in order to be respected as a man.

One day when other boys had great sport shooting passenger pigeons, John begged his father for the use of his pistol. And Netnokwa agreed.

With the big pistol in hand, John set off, almost trembling with excitement. He shot once, then carried his pigeon home victorious. Then the father gave John a gun of his own. Later, John learned to trap marten as skillfully as the young men who had ridiculed him. So, at the age of twelve, his family looked upon him as a man. He had, indeed, become The Falcon.

But Netnokwa worried for fear Indian strangers might kill this white son, or some white trader would steal him from her. So she determined to go to the Red River of the North. With her chief's flag waving at the bow of her canoe, she led a brigade of six canoes. At the entrance to Lake Superior she came upon a fur company schooner loading for its trip to Grand Portage at the western end of the lake. In order to travel lightly, she put her baggage aboard the ship. Skimming over the lake, Netnokwa's band reached the great trading post ten days ahead of the fur company's ship.

Netnokwa and her band of Indians arrived at Grand Portage in time for the June gathering of fur trade men. Indians swarmed into the post with their heavy loads of winter furs, meeting there to trade with white merchants arriving from Montreal in large canoes filled with trade goods.

But now, John's father and one of Netnokwa's sons had become ill. Carrying the two invalids and the baggage over the nine-mile portage to Pigeon River proved extremely difficult, but finally they reached Fort Charlotte at the end of the portage. Here they set about making the smaller canoes they would need on the inland waters where they must often carry the canoes over rapids and land. While they worked at making canoes, the father died.

The canoes built, Netnokwa's band continued. After they had passed only two portages, the invalid brother knew he was dying. The rest of the band continued on toward the Red River, leaving Netnokwa alone with her sons. After the brother died, they returned to Grand Portage and suffered through an extremely bad winter, living outside the fort and nearly starving.

The following summer they lived on Isle Royale, and John hunted and fished, becoming the provider for the fatherless family. Netnokwa allowed him complete freedom and John realized that he could now escape from the Indians. But because he believed all his white family and friends had been killed by Manito-o-geezik and his friends, John found himself questioning whether he really would be happy with white people again. Indian men had learned to respect him, no longer ridiculed him. Here in the great woods he had freedom; among the whites he would labor hard in the fields. Labor he had come to believe, as his Indian family and friends believed, was for squaws.

Five years now a captive, John Tanner had become an Indian in his ways. He spoke their language, scarcely remembered the English of his childhood. He wore his hair in a long braid. He dressed in a breechclout, leggings and moccasins. He was more Falcon, the Indian, than John Tanner, the white man.

* * * * * * * * *

Netnokwa eventually led her family as far north as Lake Winipeg. And there, following the Red River southward, Falcon hunted beavers, from October until late February each year. Netnokwa traded these thick and beautiful pelts to white traders. That winter along the Red River, Falcon killed his first bear—and all the hunters of Netnokwa's band gathered to celebrate his accomplishment and to feast upon the bear.

But hard times came that same winter and an Ottawa chief, a relative of Netnokwa, came to help her family. He promised to provide for her if she and her daughter and daughter-in-law would care for his lodge. Netnokwa agreed and the chief led them, after two months of trudging on showshoes, to his lodge on the Mouse River. There they spent a miserable winter because of the extreme cold.

Until he was twenty, Falcon and Netnokwa and her family wandered about the Assiniboine and Red Rivers and occasionally to Grand Portage. Sometimes they joined with other Indians—theymight be Crees, Assiniboine, Ottowa, or Chippewa. Through times of near starvation or sudden plenty, and times when Netnokwa's own family members would leave her, Falcon stayed with his Indian mother. Often he was the only hunter to find food for her family. And whether Falcon trapped many beavers or few, it was Netnokwa who dressed the skins, claimed their ownership and traded for them.

Their trading brought them to Pembina, and one winter they lived outside the fort. Here as in other trading posts, the white trader kept his supply of much-diluted rum and Falcon saw how foolishly the Indian would trade his furs for the liquor. Falcon watched the drunken frolics in which Indian men, women, and children joined; during a wild brawl, an Indian sometimes killed his best friend or his wife or child.

Netnokwa's strong spirit broke when her own son deserted her. She began to drink, trading Falcon's furs for rum. Finally, Falcon himself joined with the Indians in their drinking, and afterwards felt ashamed.

Now and then at the trading posts, white men recognized that the blue-eyed Falcon was of their own race and they would invite him to return to his own people. Yet, despite the hunger and cold he often endured with Netnokwa, Falcon refused their offers. He knew he was a hunter at heart.

Then one day when he was twenty-one, Netnokwa told him, "It is time for you to have a wife. I am old. I can no longer dress all your skins and make your moccasins."

Falcon suddenly realized that he really wanted to marry a white woman. When Netnokwa made arrangements with a chief for his daughter to be Falcon's wife, Falcon refused. No young woman that Netnokwa suggested met his approval.

The following winter, however, he met Dawn Sky and found himself attracted to her. Netnokwa did not think that Dawn Sky would make a good wife for Falcon. She said Dawn Sky was a trouble-maker. But in the end, Falcon married her.

The steady trapping of beaver to trade with the white men could only bring the beaver to near extermination, and Falcon found he must hunt further southward and westward into the prairies. He traded furs for a horse and learned to hunt buffalo. He found himself wanting more and more to hunt by himself, to be alone.

While he joined with Cree and Chippewa bands to go where the dreaded Sioux claimed territory, he also learned that increasingly the Indians held him as one apart from themselves. He did not accept the religious teachings of the Shawnee prophets and shamans and this angered Dawn Sky and her relatives who thereby blamed him for misfortunes that beset them. He had become a renowned hunter and for this he was envied, but he was a white man to be hated with the rest of the Long Knives who were ruining the Indian's way of life.

When an Assiniboine Indian stole his horse from him, Falcon determined to go alone in search of it. Nothing would keep him from going directly to Assiniboine camps. For a time Netnokwa's youngest son went with him, but when they neared the first Assiniboine camp, he deserted. Falcon continued alone until in one village he found the horse thieves and, surprisingly, he was able to bring back not only one, but two horses. He gave one horse to a friend. Then when that horse died, Falcon gave the friend his own horse.

As Netnokwa had prophesied, Dawn Sky proved a trouble-maker. At one time, she deserted Falcon and left him to care for their three small children. Rather than remain with unfriendly relatives, Falcon took his children into the deep woods where he built a lodge and cared for them through the winter. The next spring Dawn Sky returned to him. But when she again left him, Falcon took another Indian woman to be his wife and to care for his children.

* * * * * * * * *

Pembina had become the trading post where Falcon usually traded. One day while he was out hunting, he met a white trapper who urged him to leave the Indians and return to his own people. This trapper told Falcon that he had heard that someone from the Tanner family had searched as far as Mackinac for him. Falcon replied that he had few furs of value to trade with the whites, that he had a wife and family to feed. He must stay with them.

In 1812 the first of hundreds of Scottish farmers and their wives and children arrived at the forks of the Red and Assiniboine Rivers. They had come to settle around Fort Douglas on land owned by Lord Selkirk, a Scottish nobleman. They nearly starved that first winter, and the second year they built a small fort near Fort Pembina. There the governor of this Selkirker colony hired Falcon to hunt buffalo to provide meat for the settlers. Falcon delivered the meat of forty buffaloes and for this he was paid $310.

The following summer he took his family to Rainy Lake where they spent a pleasant summer of hunting, caring for cornfields, gathering wild rice, and fishing. Unknown to him, a savage war had broken out between the men of the Hudson's Bay Company at Fort Douglas and the men of the North West Company at Pembina. And Lord Selkirk himself had come to America with a hundred hired soldiers to protect his settlers.

The North West Company men captured Fort Douglas where the Selkirkers lived at the northern end of Red River. They expected Lord Douglas's soldiers to attack them there and that his soldiers would come up the usual lakes-and-river route from Grand Portage and on to Fort Douglas.

But at Rainy Lake, Lord Douglas learned of the blue-eyed Indian, the skilled hunter who had supplied his settlers with buffalo meat. He hired Falcon to guide his small army.

Instead of taking the soldiers the expected route, Falcon took them a dangerous way, across swamps and quagmires, where no other white man had ever gone. This brought them to Pembina where in the dead of night, Falcon and the soldiers captured the fort without firing a shot.

They then went north along the Red River toward Fort Douglas. In the dark of night, Falcon and one other man made an "Indian" ladder of a tree with branches lopped off and climbed over the fort walls; the soldiers followed after and so they captured Fort Douglas without firing a gun.

Lord Douglas paid Falcon well for his services and told him he should return to his own people. He offered to take Falcon back with him to the States and even to England. But the idea of going back to live with whites now almost terrified Falcon. He spoke the Indian language, knew little of the English of his childhood. He knew only Indian ways, little of the white man's ways.

He returned to his family at Rainy Lake and suffered with them through another winter. In the spring, after his wife's relatives had tried to kill him, Falcon decided it would be better for him to find his own people again. White men at the North West Company's trading posts as well hated him for helping Lord Selkirk's soldiers. In a land where game had been hunted to near extermination, even a hunter as skilled as he would have difficulty making a living.

Thus in the summer of 1817, the white boy turned Indian man took his small canoe and set out alone to go back to find and live with his own relatives again.

* * * * * * * * *

For nearly thirty years Falcon tried to become John Tanner, the white man. He learned to speak the English language again and dictated the story of his life with the Indians to a physician, Dr. Edwin James, at Mackinac. John Tanner's *Narrative*, a book that he himself could not read, was published in 1830. John Tanner also helped Dr. James translate the New Testament into Chippewa.

He early learned that his family had not been murdered, though his father was now dead. He found his brother Edward still searching for him, and Edward took him home to his relatives. The relatives received him with hospitality. But John Tanner—a sick man much of the time—could tell that they did not truly accept him as one of their own.

He yearned for his own children and returned to the Red River and brought three of them back. Many Indians traded at Mackinac and lived in the country nearby, but Mackinac was under the control of whites. So where the Long Knives and the Indians were together, John Tanner tried to work as an interpreter and trader.

But he found among the whites the same distrust that he had known among the Indians along Red River. White people could not accept this "white Indian" who lived in an Indian hut and followed Indian ways of daily living. The whites took his children from him to civilize them, and John Tanner lived a recluse, moving to Sault St. Marie in 1828.

He felt uncomfortable in white man's clothes or in a white man's house. Thinking that white men would accept him if he had a white wife, he married a white woman at Detroit. But after he brought her to the squalor of his Indian hut and she bore him a child, she ran away from him and later divorced him.

The last known of John Tanner was in 1846 at Sault St. Marie. Despised and suspected of a murder later confessed by a white soldier, he escaped into the woods when soldiers and bloodhounds set after him.

And so John Tanner, the white Indian called The Falcon, disappeared, a lonely, heartbroken and bitter man. Too much an Indian in his ways, white people would not accept him; and because John Tanner was a man of the hated white race, the Indians would not tolerate him. In the wilderness, hiding from his own kind, the white Indian lived out his life.

4 - Cart Boy

Fifteen-year-old George Northrop had a dream: some day he would walk, all by himself, from Minnesota and all across the western wilderness to the Pacific Ocean and from there right up to the Bering Strait that separated Alaska from Siberia. It mattered not how many men and boys ridiculed his ambition. George kept dreaming his dream.

When his father died that year of 1852, George refused to depend on his relatives for a living. The father had sent him to a good school and George had learned to keep accounts, to read Latin, and to write well. So George left central New York and went to Saint Paul and from there on to Saint Cloud, then a frontier town.

But George wanted to get into the wilderness and make friends with the Indians. So he hired as a trader's clerk at a post on Big Stone Lake. Here he met the Yankton Sioux Indians who came to the post to trade, and George eagerly set about learning their Dacotah language. Sioux Indians ranged all over the plains westward where some day George would go on that hike, so he wanted to be able to talk to Indians he would meet.

One day George did something no grown man at the trading post dared do: he took a wagon load of goods and drove off alone into Yankton Sioux country to trade. After reaching an Indian encampment, he did quite a bit of trading when he caught sight of a brave stealing a blanket from his wagon.

Young George ran right after the Indian and wrestled the blanket away from him. This surprised the other Indians so much they laughed at the thief and showed they admired the white boy. When George finished trading all his goods, he drove back to Big Stone Lake.

Later, he learned that the Indian thief planned to kill him. George went directly to the brave and quietly explained that he wanted to be friends. The brave then said, "I did not mind that you took the blanket away from me, but you disgraced me in front of my people." Finally, however, he became friends with George.

For three years, as Goerge worked as a trader's clerk, he learned to speak Dacotah and to know the ways of the Sioux people.

He became an expert rifleman. Alone or with others, he went further and further westward, hunting or trading. One of the dogs at the trading post became George's constant companion no matter where he went.

So one day in 1855, George decided the time had come to start walking across the wilderness to Fort Benton, Montana, and then on to the Pacific and Alaska.

At Saint Cloud he bought a light handcart with large wheels. On it he piled food and utensils he would need on his long journey. And early one morning eighteen-year-old George Northrop set out with his dog and cart on his great adventure.

Pulling his cart behind him, his faithful dog bringing up the rear, George on his second day met a solitary old man living beside a pleasant stream. The man greeted George warmly, then asked, "Where are you going, young man?"

As though it was nothing unusual, George replied, "I am going to Fort Benton in Montana and from there to the Pacific and from there to Alaska."

The man stared in unbelief. "Young man, that is impossible. You will not get very far out on the prairies before some Sioux will lift your scalp!"

"Oh," said George, calmly, "I am well acquainted with the Sioux. I can talk their language. I worked out at the Big Stone Lake trading post, and I have traded with them and gone out into their country. The Yankton Sioux know me and they call me Chan-pa-hmi-hma Yu-sdo-ha and that means 'The Man That Draws The Cart'."

The old man shook his head. "You don't know what you are trying to do. It's thousands of miles out there. The wheels on your cart will wear out or break down. You just can't do such an impossible thing. No, stay here with me and rest and think better of it!"

George spent the night at the man's cabin. He awoke at daybreak. He thanked his kindly host for his hospitality, whistled to his dog, and grasped the cart handles.

The old man shook his head again. "Son, I am afraid I will never see you again. No one can do what you want to do and stay alive. It's impossible!"

George smiled and said, "I like to try the impossible."

He picked up the trail left by the Stevens' Survey* two years earlier.

George had no trouble tracing this Stevens route because the Red River carts, the wagons, and horses had left a well-marked trail.

Day followed day for George and his dog. Not a sign of any human beings did they see. Each night with his faithful companion beside him, George lay down to sleep under his cart. At dawn he continued on his way, the Stevens trail so far clear before him.

---

* With the discovery of gold in California in 1849, thousands of people had boarded ships that took them around the tip of South America, then up the Pacific Coast to the San Francisco area. Other thousands of goldseekers went west on the Oregon Trail.

Americans decided that what was needed was a railway across the continent, connecting the East with the West. So four possible routes for a railway were then explored, and the northernmost route would go across the plains from Saint Paul and over the mountains to Puget Sound in Washington Territory. Isaac Stevens had been appointed governor of Washington Territory, so on his way there his expedition explored a possible railway route. In what is now North Dakota, the Stevens Expedition took a route which many years later the Great Northern Railway would follow.

Then the monotony of the prairie and the loneliness began to trouble him. The dog, too, would leave his place behind the cart and come up to George, look wistfully up at him, not understanding this long and tedious journeying. George would speak gently to the dog and this seemed to soothe him. Yet George, too, began to feel strange, hearing his own voice, solitary on the prairie, with no answering speech.

Where the prairies began to rise up in to the Coteau du Missouri, the Stevens trail became less distinct. For a month now, George had pulled his cart behind him, the swish of the grass as he trod through it almost the only sound to hear. And in all those days, though George scanned every way, not an Indian did he spy.

Then one day because George could read the prairie as he could read a book, he found tracks -- tracks not of peaceful Sioux but of Sioux in war parties. The tracks led northward. Were these Sioux scouring the hills of the Coteau for any Cree or Assiniboine coming down to hunt buffalo on the prairies the Sioux claimed as their own? To meet with such a war party could mean death.

He awoke one morning to discover everything in his cart had disappeared. Now he knew that though he had seen no Indians, they had seen him. His only chance to stay alive would be to somehow reach the nearest trading post -- way back at Big Stone Lake.

He had no further need of the handcart and left it there on the prairie. Boy and dog started the long hike toward Big Stone Lake. Having no longer food or water with him, George soon thirsted and hungered. But the next day, reaching a pond, he and the dog found frogs. He had no way in which he could light a fire and broil frog legs -- and the Indians would quickly spot the smoke. Famished, George followed his dog's example and ate the flesh of the frog raw.

As much by night as by day, George and his dog stole steadily in the direction of Big Stone Lake. Four days they lived on raw frogs, and finally thirty-nine days after leaving Saint Cloud, they reached the trading post at Big Stone Lake.

The story of George Northrop's handcart expedition spread over the nation. Even the *New York Tribune* joined lesser newspapers in reporting the adventure. But once it was over, George did not like to talk about it -- he wanted to forget the terrible loneliness he had experienced on that solitary journey.

George W. Northrop became a famed frontiersman, respected by Indians and white men alike for his extraordinary marksmanship with a gun. He several times guided parties of Englishmen who came to hunt buffalo. He served as a guard on Red River steamboats and carried mail by dogsled. He served as a scout for General Crook and Major General Thomas. Then in 1864 when General Sully pursued the Sioux who were believed to have taken part in the Sioux Uprising in 1862, George Northrop was called to be a scout for Sully. On this expedition, he also served as a correspondent for the *Saint Paul Press*.

On July 23 at the Battle of Killdeer Mountain, Sioux arrows killed The Man-That-Draws-The-Handcart. And George Northrop was buried there in an unmarked grave.

5 - Lord Milton Rides The Red

A hundred and fifty years ago, when the buffalo still roamed the western plains, wealthy Europeans came to America to hunt or to share in the excitement of exploring places yet unseen by white men. A number of noblemen joined in this kind of sport.

In England the frail and spoiled young Lord Milton wanted to go into the Canadian wilds and find a new route to the Cariboo Gold Diggings near the northern reaches of the Fraser River. His parents, Lord and Lady Fitzwilliam, considered that such outdoor adventuring might make their son stronger. However, because of young William's poor health, they knew he could not set out alone on such a bold venture.

But at Cambridge University, Milton had made friends with an athletic young man who had just become a doctor. Doctor Walter Cheadle, four years older than the 22-year Milton, agreed to go with the young lord and be the guardian of his health.

In 1861 when Dr. Cheadle and Lord Milton left England on a steamer, thousands of goldseekers traveled the Pacific Ocean by steamer up to the Fraser River. Lord Milton's goal was to find a new way westward from Fort Garry on the Red River of the North. Neither he nor his companion realized what a vast extent of prairies, forests and Rocky Mountains stretched beyond Fort Garry to the Cariboo Gold Diggings.

While crossing the Atlantic, Lord Milton met a Mr. Messiter who was also bound for Fort Garry. Messiter planned to hunt buffalo and grizzly bears. He carried with him five rifles, three revolvers and a gun, plus mosquito nets, gloves and all sorts of items to make wilderness life more comfortable. When the three young men reached Chicago by lake steamer, Messiter decided he would join with Lord Milton and Cheadle.

The three took a train to LaCrosse, Wisconsin, then went up the Mississippi by steamboat to St. Paul. Here they hired a spring wagon to transport them to St. Cloud where Lord Milton bought a dog for twenty dollars. They continued their way to the Hudson's Bay Company trading post at Georgetown on the Red River.

At Georgetown, they rented a birchbark canoe and bought another one for six dollars. They loaded into these canoes all of Messiter's guns and equipment and a supply of food. Since Red River flows north to Fort Garry in Canada, the three considered that a pleasant and easy journey would soon bring them to the fort where they would outfit themselves for the great adventure westward.

They did not know that the Red River is the crookedest river in the world, and that one must travel twice as many miles by Red River as by land. By this time, Messiter and Milton began to argue about anything and everything as they started their leisurely paddling.

The bickering continued even when rainstorms doused them, and their canoes began to leak. They bailed water and argued about how much the dog, Rover, actually weighed. Messiter had the only watch and when it stopped, they argued about what time it might be. When the rain ceased occasionally, mosquitoes swarmed over them no matter how they tried to protect themselves with Messiter's mosquito netting. Around each bend of the river, they must steer their canoes while mosquitoes fed on them.

When they reached the Goose Rapids, they met the *International,* one of the earliest steamboats on the river. The churning sternwheeler almost swamped their canoes as the three paddled furiously out of its way. By now their soft hands blistered. When they pulled their canoes to shore to rest and get some food to eat, they found their food had all spoiled.

Hungry, they continued on their way, faithful Rover following them along the river bank. No game birds or animals showed themselves as marks for one of Messiter's expensive guns. One time, thinking a hostile Sioux rustled some bushes, Messiter took aim and nearly shot Rover.

The three men knew nothing about living in the wilderness. Rover caught one of the thousands of passenger pigeons that then inhabited the area, and this small bird the three fried in their pan and ate ravenously. Then they broke the handle on the frying pan as well as the axe handle. This gave Messiter and Milton more to sputter about.

Still hungry, they looked about for anything that might have flesh. They decided to catch frogs and in this sport, Rover joined them. They fried frog legs in their broken frying pan after scrounging among the trees along the river for dry, dead twigs and branches.

Then it rained almost steadily. This, however, gave them relief from the tormenting mosquitoes. When the sun beat down on hot muggy days, they tried to dry out soaked matches that would no longer light. They caught a few small fish in the river and these with frogs and an occasional pigeon provided them with scarce enough food to survive.

But, finally, on August 7, 1862, each of them suffering from boils and insect bites and nearly starving, they reached the stone walls of Fort Garry.

The disagreeable trip down the Red River of the North was but a small part of the thousands of miles they would have to travel to reach the Cariboo Gold Diggings. But on the Red River they passed their first tests in wilderness survival. At Fort Garry they decided not to return to the comforts of Old England but to continue with their goal.

Soon after he had hunted some buffaloes, Messiter decided to go home to England, but Lord Milton and Dr. Cheadle determined to explore that westward route to the gold fields. Milton hired the first of several Indian and halfbreed guides and bought supplies. Had they known the hardships, suffering, and dangers they would endure, perhaps, like Messiter, they too would have returned to England. Thanks to their hardy and wilderness-wise guides, particularly an Assiniboine and his wife, Lord Milton and his guardian finally reached the Cariboo goldfield. They did not search for gold, for despite savage storms and bitter cold, near starvation, and almost losing their lives in a raging river, they had accomplished what they had set out to do.

They left for England in March, 1864. They never returned to the land of their great adventure, but in the northern Canadian Rockies not far from Yellowhead Pass, Mount Cheadle and Mount Milton memorialize two men who did not turn back.

6 - Crane Hunt

The goldseekers broke camp that July morning of 1862 at a place near what is now Velva, North Dakota. The corral of wagons had kept the oxen and cows safe through a night when prairie wolves had howled as they stalked about the camp. Four guards who had stood watch now lay down to get some sleep in wagons rumbling northwest along the Souris (Mouse) River.

Most of the 117 men and 13 women of that Fisk Expedition wanted to reach Fort Benton, Montana, because gold had been discovered in the West. Others, like Captain James L. Fisk and the soldiers sent along to protect the emigrants, would turn back from Montana and return to Fort Abercrombie. With them also was Dr. Dibb, a physician sent along to care for any who might become sick or injured.

No one was sick or injured that July morning, so Dr. Dibb and two other men decided they would get on their horses and go hunting. They had seen thousands of buffaloes grazing as well as antelope and deer.

Just a few days earlier, Captain Fisk, riding ahead of the expedition, had sighted a grizzly bear. Other men joined in the chase and killed the 600-pound female bear. They brought it to camp and afterwards all enjoyed a feast of bear meat.

Days before, Pierre Bottineau, the guide, had been thrown off his horse when it stepped into a badger hole. So now as the three hunters rode southward into hilly country, they watched for holes dug by badgers, foxes and wolves.

There was nothing Dr. Dibb enjoyed more than to hunt and he soon strayed off alone, certain he could find his way back over the trail of the slow-moving expedition. He had done so before. With Captain Fisk and Pierre Bottineau, he had sighted four buffalo bulls and ridden after them. Bottineau and his trained buffalo-hunting horse quickly dropped one bull to the ground, and soon after Captain Fisk killed the second. Dr. Dibb's horse, unused to buffalo hunting, shied away whenever they neared the bull he wanted to shoot. But after a long chase, Dr. Dibb managed to shoot the buffalo, and late that night he returned with the bull's bushy tail to prove his success.

Now far in the distance lay a marsh, and Dr. Dibb's keen eye caught sight of two specks of white. He urged his horse onward, hopeful that he had spotted a pair of whooping cranes. About the campfires at night, he had heard about these magnificent birds. Full five feet high, a crane had a wing spread of seven to eight feet. One of those wings, Dr. Dibb decided, would be quite a trophy to bring back to camp, a trophy more unusual than a buffalo tail!

As he neared the marsh, he saw that indeed the two specks of white were cranes. He stopped his horse and watched as the cranes waded on stilt-like legs. Into the water, one long-necked crane dropped its head and soon out came the head, a frog in its long dagger-like beak. A few gulps and the crane had swallowed the frog.

But the other crane, its long neck erect and its head swiveling about for signs of danger, must have caught sight of Dr. Dibb and his horse. With a few long strides of those stilt-like legs, it rose into the air with its great wings flapping in graceful rhythm. And as the fleeing crane rose higher into the air, he trumpeted his long, booming call and his mate followed close behind.

Dr. Dibb raised his gun, but too late. He watched as the cranes disappeared over a nearby hill. Though he could no longer see the birds, he followed the sound of the crane's whooping.

The whooping stopped as Dr. Dibb rode to the top of the hill and saw another marsh about half a mile beyond. Again he saw the two cranes.

Ah, this time he would be more careful to stay hidden from the cranes' sight! A wooded ravine led down from a hill and into the marsh. He would go behind that hill, tie his horse to a tree, then slowly sneak down the ravine and get as close as possible to the cranes.

Half an hour later, his horse tethered, Dr. Dibb crept down the ravine, hopeful the cranes had not flown away. He heard no trumpeting.

He emerged from the ravine and into soggy humps of tall grass. One slow step at the time, he crouched through clumps of cattails. Suddenly both cranes came into clear view. Stealthily, he slipped his rifle to his shoulder. He pulled the trigger and to his amazement both cranes fell.

He had killed two whooping cranes with one ball! Now truly he would have a story to tell back at camp! And instead of a bushy buffalo tail, he would bring two cranes.

But scarcely had he carried the cranes to dry land when thunder rumbled overhead. He watched dark rain clouds quickly approaching. He cut off the large wings from one bird, then held them like an umbrella over himself when the rain poured down.

As he sat there under the crane wings, he was glad his horse was safely tethered. Once the rain stopped, he would tie the cranes to the saddle and head back for camp.

Then he suddenly realized he had lost his sense of direction. The clouds hid the sun. So even after the rain ceased, he could not tell which way was north, which way was west. Darkness began to fall. He heard prairie wolves howling, closer and closer.

Fire! He must have a campfire! Wolves and coyotes and bears stayed away from fire! But he had no matches, no flints with him. Up the ravine, he managed to find some twigs and bits of dry bark and grass as he puzzled frantically over how he could start a fire.

Desperately he rubbed some gunpowder into a dry handkerchief and he set this afire by discharging the contents of his gun into it. Slowly, the dry grass caught fire from the burning handkerchief, then the little twigs and bits of bark. Dr. Dibb put on larger and larger twigs and branches and finally had a fire over which he broiled some meat he cut from a crane. After he had eaten this, he search for more and more branches for a fire he must keep burning through the night. Howling wolves and coyotes had come closer and closer.

He brought his horse nearby, tying it to the saddle. Then he lay down near the fire, the crane wings spread over him for warmth and to protect him from an occasional spattering of rain. Sleep could hardly come what with the wolves circling close enough that his horse would snort in fear. Whenever the fire began to die down, Dr. Dibb got up and added a few branches, hopeful his supply of firewood would last until daybreak. Surely then the wolves would retreat!

Morning came at last and with it the sun. Weak from hunger, Dr. Dibb broiled some more crane meat for his breakfast. Then tying what remained of the birds to his saddle, he mounted his horse and rode northward.

Much to his relief, he found the heavily-marked trail over which the wagons, oxen, cows and horses had traveled. Since the expedition usually covered twenty miles a day, and he had been away for over a day, he would have to ride fast to overtake them.

About noon he caught sight of a party of horsemen rapidly approaching him. In a short while fifteen men rode up to him, each of them holding out to him a haversack of bread and buffalo tongue. They circled about his crane-laden horse, astonished.

"What kind of bird be they?" asked one man.

"Whooping crane," said a soldier. Then turning to Dr. Dibb he asked, "Must've taken a few shots to get the two of 'em."

"Nah," said Dr. Dibb, grinning, "Got them both with one ball."

"You don't say!" said the soldier. "Don't recollect ever hearing of anybody getting two big birds like that with one shot. And cranes, they're hard to get near enough to shoot."

Looking carefully at Dr. Dibb, another soldier remarked, "Say, what with all the rain we've had, and you being out in the open all the time, how come you're not soaked through?"

"Oh," said Dr. Dibb as he held a wing over his head, "I just shot me an umbrella!"

7 - Mystery Hole

About ten miles north of the town of Killdeer, steep and craggy hills form "Takahouty," the Sioux Indian name for "the place where they killed the deer." White men call these high-rising hills the Killdeer Mountains.

Unusual rock formations bear the names of Signet Rock, Three Old Maids, and Eagle Rock -- and near these atop one hill is the mystery hole. Because a smoky fog rose out of this cavernous hole on cold days, the Indians named it Medicine Hole.

When white men first settled the region, some crawled several hundred feet down the Medicine Hole and found entrances to other underground openings and caves, one a large cavern room. Over the years, people fascinated by the stories and legends about Medicine Hole came to peer down its dark passage. Not wanting to venture down into the hole, they amused themselves by rolling rocks or tossing stones into the hole so they could hear the bouncing echoes of the rocks dropping and hurtling down the twisted passageway. Also Medicine Hole has been dynamited twice, first to plug it, later to try to open it. Today, because of all the rocks thrown down inside, passageways once open are plugged.

One mystery about Medicine Hole has persisted ever since 1864. Two years before, Sioux Indians on reservations in Minnesota had not received their promised money payments and rations of food from the U.S. Government. Angry and hungry, and knowing that most white soldiers were fighting in the Civil War, they decided to rise up and drive white settlers away from lands that had been their hunting grounds for

4 - Medicine Hole on top of Killdeer Mountain.
Photo by Sheldon Green

centuries. In August, 1862, they killed several hundred white settlers and took three hundred captive. When word spread of this uprising, other bands of Sioux attacked whites on the western plains.

In September, a force of soldiers led by General Henry Sibley drove the raiding Indians out of Minnesota. The Indians fled westward onto the Dakota prairies. Then two army expeditions, the first led by Sibley in 1863 and the second a year later by General Alfred Sully, pursued the Indians into Dakota and attacked several Indian camps.

In late July, 1864, Sully learned that about 6000 Sioux warriors and their families had camped at the foot of the Killdeer Mountains. Sully's 2200 soldiers attacked the Indian camp. The Indians had some guns but most fought with bows and arrows. When Sully fired his cannon into the camp, the Indian warriors retreated, helping their women and children to escape up the Killdeer Mountains and into the Badlands breaks beyond.

When night fell, cavalrymen surrounded the hill on which a band of Indian men stood ground. The soldiers decided they would wait until morning when they would climb this Killdeer Mountain and kill the warriors there.

Dawn came. The soldiers climbed warily toward the top expecting arrows and gunfire. Once they reached the summit, they found not one warrior waiting to fight. But there on top of Killdeer Mountain they came upon a large hole out of which wind came up.

Sully's expedition continued westward, and about a week later they came upon a band of Indians -- the same Indians that the cavalrymen had surrounded on Killdeer Mountain.

Had the Indians escaped down the Medicine Hole? Did the passageways below Medicine Hole connect with caverns and openings through which the Indians found their way out into the open?

Until the rocks plugging Medicine Hole have been removed, and the underground explored, we cannot know.

8 - Exit Uncle Buffalo

In 1869 two orphan brothers came from Germany to join older brothers who lived at Morris, Minnesota. In New York City, the two boys waited an entire day in the railway station before they could continue on their way.

But, somehow, while they waited, they learned about Buffalo Bill Cody. Hero to thousands of red-blooded American boys of that day, Buffalo Bill traveled the country with his Wild West Show, and newspapers proclaimed him the champion of all buffalo hunters.

Out on the great plains westward from Minnesota, the two boys were told, the buffaloes roamed in great herds -- by the millions, even thousands of them reported in a single herd. Yes, a man could shoot buffalo and sell the hide for a dollar apiece. By the time the brothers got on the train, they had decided they would be buffalo hunters.

But once arrived in Minnesota, they realized they could not go hunting buffaloes right away. They must earn money to repay their brothers for their fare across the Atlantic and the train from New York. They must learn to speak English if they were going to travel about the West hunting buffaloes, and they must be able to buy hunting equipment. For four years, the boys worked on farms the greater part of the time and in winter months hunted muskrat and mink. Then when Frederick, the older of the two, was sixteen, the two headed west with a wagon team and rifles.

5 - The Indian's "Uncle Buffalo" grazing in Theodore Roosevelt National Park.

6 - A "still hunt" or "buffalo stand," such as Doc Zahl used. Painting by J. H. Moser.

By 1873 Minnesota had become a state and what is now North Dakota was part of Dakota Territory. That year the Northern Pacific Railway had been built as far west as Bismarck, and land-hungry homeseekers followed the train settling the land. To find the great herds of buffalo, the Zahl boys would have to go on into Montana Territory.

Their first day at Fort Sully, they decided to try their luck hunting buffaloes. They discovered a small herd grazing along a creek just a few miles west of the Fort. Excitedly, they sneaked within easy shooting distance of the animals. Frederick took careful aim and fired at a huge bull. Wounded, the bull thundered away across the prairie, and all the rest of the buffaloes followed in wild stampede.

The boys returned empty-handed from their first buffalo hunt. They considered Buffalo Bill to be an even greater hero than they first had thought.

At camp that night, Frederick met an old half-breed buffalo hunter. He told the man how, though he had shot the big buffalo, it had just run away and taken every other buffalo with it.

The veteran hunter listened, then shook his head.

"You aim at buffalo's head?"

"Yes."

"That is no way to hunt buffalo. Buffalo head is tough and hard. You only sting buffalo."

"How then do you shoot a buffalo?" Frederick wanted to know.

"Shoot buffalo in paunch -- in small space near hip. Then buffalo get sick. He lay down. Other buffaloes not notice. Keep eating grass. Then you shoot more buffalo in paunch. And they lay down. Soon they die."

The next afternoon, Frederick and his brother came upon a large herd of buffaloes several miles west of Fort Sully. Stealthily, and against the prairie wind, they stole within rifle range.

Frederick aimed for that small space near the hip bone of a bull and fired. He watched amazed as the animal slumped to the ground. The other buffaloes seemed not to notice but just kept on grazing. Now the younger brother leveled his rifle and sighted at the spot below the back and to the fore of the hip bone, and the bullet spat from his gun. The buffalo settled down into the tall grass. In just a short while, the brothers' careful aim brought a dozen bulls lying upon the ground. Yet the herd went on feeding.

Deciding they had enough buffaloes to keep them busy skinning the rest of the day, the brothers walked closer to the herd. At sight of them, the buffaloes charged wildly away and the boys set to work skinning their first buffalo hides.

Remembering the counsel of the half-breed, Frederick went into the Black Hills region to hunt buffalo for a living. Frank, however, decided he could make more money working in a hotel.

As Frederick continued his hunting, he became more and more expert. However, the quality of buffalo coats was best in the fall when cold weather approached, so he took other jobs during the warm months of spring and summer.

For a time, the two brothers operated a woodyard on the Yellowstone River, selling firewood to the river steamers then going as far west as Fort Benton. Though they could make more money chopping wood than hunting buffalo, the lure of the hunt never dimmed for the two brothers. That fall they both followed the buffalo migrating southward for the winter.

Frederick's reputation for marksmanship soon spread. Ranchers, river men, woodhawks, cowboys and hunters liked to tell about the adventures of this man who could keep four skinners busy when few buffalo hunters could use two skinners. They called him "Doc" and this name stuck with Frederick the rest of his life.

Rich men from the East eagerly hired Doc Zahl to scout for their hunting parties. Doc took Teddy Roosevelt on his first buffalo hunt.

In 1882 after Doc was appointed a deputy U.S. marshal, he and his brother invested their savings in a hunters lodge at the junction of the Musselshell and Missouri Rivers. This was where the buffalo crossed on their annual fall migration. Their first year at the lodge the Zahl brothers did a profitable business providing lodging and supplies for an increasing number of buffalo hunters.

The next fall hundreds of men arrived in Montana for the sport of shooting buffalo. After the hunt, they wanted to return East to show off a shaggy-haired trophy. They crowded into the Zahl lodge ready for the buffaloes which usually reached that area in late September. Doc and his brother extended full credit for supplies because they would be repaid when the hunt was over.

September passed. Not a buffalo appeared.

October days dragged by for men who had often beheld the spectacle of hills and prairie covered with a dark sea of buffaloes. Before the month ended, many of the discouraged hunters returned East, for no buffaloes had yet come down the centuries-old route from the Canadian prairies.

In late December Doc and his brother were left alone at their outpost, most of the supplies they had sold never paid for.

Never again would great herds of buffaloes come thundering and rumbling across hills and buttes, down prairie valleys and coulees to winter in the warm grasslands further south. Never again would these monarchs of the plains return with the spring to the vast feeding grounds of the north.

Stunned, the Zahl brothers went to Terry, Montana Territory, and there opened a trading store. Eventually, Frank returned to live near his brothers at Morris, Minnesota. Doc spent two years at Fort Buford, supplying the military post with game that he hunted. He also hauled fort supplies from Bismarck, using sixteen mules on a jerk line.

He next moved to nearby Williston where he served as the first county treasurer of Williams County. He later operated a ranch near the town named Zahl in honor of this champion of buffalo hunters.

For, actually, Doc Zahl outdid Buffalo Bill Cody. The greatest number of buffaloes that Buffalo Bill ever shot in one stand was 69; Doc Zahl's record was 120.

* * * * * * * * * *

Why did no buffalo that fall of 1883 come migrating down a trail that many thousands of buffalo had followed for centuries past? Doubtless, most of the buffaloes had been killed by hunters. It is also possible that the buffaloes which did not come where Doc Zahl expected them that fall had died of disease.

By this time, many ranchers had brought up large numbers of cattle from Texas where "tick fever" was common. Tick fever could kill cattle. In 1825 in eastern Nebraska an epidemic of such a disease destroyed all the buffaloes there. Another epidemic in 1858 exterminated the buffaloes in the Platte River area.

When the first white men explored into what is now North Dakota, they saw such large herds of buffalo that the hills were covered with them for miles around.

We can never really know for sure, but it has been estimated that when Columbus discovered America, somewhere between fifty and a hundred million buffaloes ranged over the plains of North America.

The plains Indians killed only as many buffaloes as they needed for food, shelter and clothing. The Spanish, French, and British traders who first came into our Missouri country did not want buffalo robes—they wanted beaver pelts. Not until the railroads began building across the United States did the real hunting of buffalo begin.

Hired hunters shot buffaloes to supply railway building crews with fresh meat. Once railway tracks had been laid, men

7 - Buffalo bone pickers bringing a load to sell.

8 - Piles of buffalo bones awaiting shipment at railway station.

from Europe and the East began riding out on trains and shooting buffaloes just for the sport of it. Then when a method was learned for making leather from buffalo hides, the slaughter of buffaloes increased yearly. Many thousands of buffalo hides were shipped down the Missouri River to Bismarck. Here for several years about 50,000 robes and hides were shipped to eastern markets on the Northern Pacific railway. Once buffalo hides were made into leather, the number shipped from Bismarck increased to 200,000 in 1882; but two years later, a single carload was the final shipment of buffalo hides, for the slaughter of Uncle Buffalo had ended.

When Dakota homesteaders first came to settle, they found the chalk-white bones of the buffalo bleaching over the prairies. Since the bones could be ground up into fertilizer or used as carbon in the refining of sugar, settlers gathered up the bones and sold them to dealers at railway stations.

Often the bone-gatherers burned off the grass to easier find the bones. Teamsters collected bones from as far back as a hundred miles from the Missouri River, hauling their loads to the river for shipment on steamers. Some of these obtained $18 a ton for crushed bones, $12 for uncrushed.

Most settlers who gathered bones were paid between $6 and $10 a ton. Homesteaders also traded the bones for groceries. Piles of bones 10 to 12 feet high, and sometimes a quarter of a mile in length, lay beside Dakota Territory railway stations.

Long before the white men nearly exterminated the buffaloes and thus destroyed the plains Indian's way of life, old Indian storytellers used to tell their little children an ancient legend of how the first buffalo, a beautiful white bull with horns and hooves of black had told the Indians:

"My tribe will come to you and your people in great numbers. Use us well, for the day will come when we shall go back into the ground again. And when we are gone, the Indian will go, too."

9 - The Professor's Palace Car

The puffing locomotive shunted the last and longest car to the railway siding, the brakemen unhitched the car, and the locomotive wheezed away.

Large and elegant letters along the top side of the railway car identified it as the "Haynes Palace Studio." Other signs painted on the outside of the car proclaimed F. Jay Haynes as the official photographer for the Northern Pacific Railway as well as the official photographer for the Yellowstone National Park.

Out from the observation deck at the rear of the palace studio car stepped a jaunty young man. He cheerfully greeted the folks gathered about. "Come aboard," he cried out, "and see for yourself!"

And so, just a few years before North Dakota became a state, young and old came aboard to inspect what would become the most famous railway car in America. They stepped up into the observation deck, then entered through glass doors into a carpeted reception room.

Mirrors and large photographs bedecked the walls here and in the 24-foot long room beyond. As they walked into this room, they saw ornate chairs and tables and several painted back-drops, the camera mounted on a tripod and covered with a large black cloth. (During those years, taking pictures with a camera seemed like some sort of magic to most people. Only photo-graphers-- and there were not many of them-- owned the heavy, large cameras and knew how to operate them.)

9 - The Haynes Palace Studio car.
Photographed by Elliott W. Hunter in 1890.

10 - Interior of Haynes Studio car.
Photograph by F. Jay Haynes, 1886.

Visitors did not go beyond the studio room, but they sometimes caught a glimpse of Jeeter, the black man, in the small rooms beyond -- a dark room, a kitchen, and sleeping quarters.

The jaunty young man who welcomed folks aboard the studio car had become so expert a photographer that folks called him "Professor" Haynes. Of course, he was not a real professor, but folks in those days often gave the title of "professor" to a man who showed unusual skill or knowledge.

Before the palace studio car arrived in a town to stay for several days, posters and advertisements had announced the time of its coming. So proud parents brought their babies or their entire families to the studio car and there they stood or sat perfectly still in front of a painted backdrop while Professor Haynes, his head under a large black cloth that covered the back of the camera, focused it and counted several seconds before the family could relax. (Snapshots and instant-picture-taking would not be developed for many more years.)

At the studio car a hunter might come wearing his buffalo coat and pose with his dog. Here the happy bride and groom had their wedding pictures taken, usually with the groom seated in a fancy chair and the bride standing beside him with one hand on his shoulder.

The immigrant homesteader who had prospered in Dakota hired Professor Haynes to bring his heavy camera equipment out to his farm, and there in front of their new house and perhaps with their new buggy and team of horses, the family would pose. If possible, the photograph would also show the barn and the granary as well. Such a picture the immigrant sent back to the Old Country to show off to his relatives and friends how he had prospered in America.

Young Frank Haynes learned the "magic" of photography at a studio in Saline, Michigan. Then in 1876 when he was 23, lured by frontier adventure, he set out for Moorhead, Minnesota, and there built himself a small studio. But he was really an outdoorsman and could not stay confined to a house, so he set out taking pictures that would tell the story of the great bonanza farms of the Red River Valley and of the steamboats that once paddled up and down the Red River. Haynes established a larger studio in Fargo, and leaving his wife and a trained helper in charge of the studio, he would go west with photographic equipment that often weighed as much as 200 pounds.

Sometimes he loaded his equipment on a mule, often he rode horseback or walked. Stagecoaches carried the Professor into frontier places. The Missouri River steamer, "The Far West," took him as far as Fort Benton, Montana. And the man then superintendent of the newly-established Yellowstone National Park invited him to photograph the wonders there. The Professor did so well that he was appointed official photographer of the Park and his pictures brought the first tourists there.

The Northern Pacific Railway people learned of the Professor's skill and invited him to ride their train as its rails advanced further west. The Professor's photographs helped prove Easterners wrong when they called the great plains the "Great American Desert." His photographs of the large bonanza farms helped bring a tide of settlers to build homes and to farm in Dakota. Young Haynes traveled with hunting expeditions and so showed the abundant wild life of the western plains.

As he roamed about with his camera, Haynes began to dream of a studio that would travel with him, a studio that could stop in prairie towns where no photographer ever came. And so he invested all his savings in what would become the Haynes Palace Studio Car. At Brainerd, Minnesota, Haynes remodeled a large Pullman car into a traveling photo studio.

Then for many years, Haynes took his studio car wherever rails could take him, mostly on the Northern Pacific tracks. Portraits of Indians, pictures of goldseekers and mining towns, photographs that told of the beauty of Alaskan, Canadian, and Pacific wildernesses, and the pioneers who first lived there -- thousands of such pictures are preserved today in museums and in books.

With him went Jeeter, his trusty cook, barber and all around helper. Both men liked to travel and hunt. When the train stopped for some emergency or to take on water, Haynes shouldered his gun and shortly returned with a prairie chicken or an elk for Jeeter to cook.

As expert with cooking as Haynes was with photography, Jeeter never failed to provide a tasty meal for both. Once when the Professor returned empty-handed from a quick prairie hunt, he found Jeeter had dinner ready. Haynes smacked his lips over the delicious meal. Afterwards, he learned he had dined on a skunk which Jeeter had shot.

10 - Hunter's Paradise

Shortly after their marriage, Douglas and Hannah Bell left Nebraska in a covered wagon and headed for Dakota Territory to hunt buffalo. September, 1881, found them at Boxelder Creek in western Dakota Territory, digging into a hill to make their first home. And to join them in their hunting, and living in the dugout, came Douglas's father, Jacob, and his brother, Bent.

They made the dugout roof of poles and covered it with untanned buffalo hides. Another large hide hung over the door opening at the front of the dugout. At the farther end of the excavation, they built a crude fireplace of stones with a smoke vent through the roof.

For this family of four, Hanah did all her cooking and baking in the fireplace and with a Dutch oven. The Bells contented themselves with roasted wild meats, sour dough bread, beans, and black coffee.

They were among the last to make a living by hunting in what is now North Dakota. During the mild winter that followed their making of the dugout, they hunted almost daily. They sometimes killed forty buffaloes in one day and Hannah rode along and helped skin the beasts. They also shot deer and antelope.

Back in the dugout, Hannah busied herself with tanning deer hides and making them into shirts, trousers, moccasins, and mittens as well as fur caps for the family. At first she worked by the light of the fireplace since they had no lamp. Then she made candles from buffalo tallow.

In March she went to Stoneville in Montana to await the birth of her first child. The following autumn and winter she and her family returned to their dugout on Boxelder Creek for another season of hunting. Fur traders came to the dugout and bought their buffalo bull hides for $1.50 each and buffalo cow hides for $2.60. They also bought buffalo meat, paying one cent a pound.

In the spring of 1883, the Bell family moved to a one-room log cabin on O'Fallon Creek in Montana where Hannah rejoiced in a real cook stove. Two years later they took up residence at Williston, North Dakota, for they could no longer make a living from hunting. The buffaloes, deer, antelopes, and elks had been hunted almost to extermination.

* * * * * * * * * *

In North Dakota today, we see cities and towns, farms, ranches, oil fields, coal mines, highways, telephone and electric power lines where once was the prairie primeval. We find it hard to believe that before the white men came here, this prairie abounded in wild life.

In that prairie primeval lived the Indian who did not kill for sport, but for food and clothing. Beavers busied themselves with water conservation by damming streams. Deep furrows of buffalo trails led from crossings and watering places and up to the high prairies.

As late as 1851, Charles Cavalier wrote: "From the top of Turtle Mountain I could see for miles and miles, and the prairie was black with buffalo ... there were simply millions upon millions of them." James Kipp, an earlier fur trader, once rode in a cart for six successive days through masses of buffaloes which allowed the cart to pass through them.

Over ninety different kinds of animals once lived in what is now North Dakota, and the Indian hunted few of them. Only one of these animals would attack a human being -- this was the grizzly bear which roved into the Badlands and the Missouri breaks. Wildcats also frequented the area.

Mink lived in abundance along the larger streams flowing into the Missouri. Otters played along the Heart and Cannonball Rivers. Muskrats built their homes in the banks of flowing streams and in sloughs, many thousands of them living in the Mouse River country.

Pronghorn antelope grazed the grasslands. White-tailed deer inhabited most of the state. Mule deer preferred the Badlands and the Little Missouri territory. Elk foraged the Missouri bottomlands. Bighorn mountain sheep climbed the sandstone and scoria buttes of the Badlands. Moose ranged the Turtle Mountains and the Pembina hills and valleys.

11 - Pyramid made from elk horns. Painting by Karl Bodmer, 1833.

Great numbers of prairie dogs dug their underground towns on sunny dry slopes in short-grass country. Before their slaughter by gas and poison, these "little farmers" as the Indians called them, populated their subterranean cities not only by thousands but even by millions.

The badger sent prairie dogs scuttling into their holes, and the rattlesnakes that sunned themselves on nearby rock ledges stole into the prairie dogs' homes. Long-legged jack rabbits scurried across the high prairies at sight of the coyote. The "Flicker-tails" (ground squirrels) kept wary eye for swooping owl or hawk. The gray wolves trailed the edges of buffalo or antelope herds to pounce upon the laggard sick or young.

In timbered glens and draws, the bobcat and lynx, the red and gray foxes, brought prey to their young. Skunks and weasels, squirrels and chipmunks, the little sage rabbits -- these the stealthy Indian watched with friendly interest as he sought for bigger game such as his "Uncle Buffalo."

The grasslands supported a tremendous population of sharp-tailed grouse, plovers, prairie chickens, and sage hens. Ducks, pelicans, swans, geese, gulls and other water fowl nested by the millions in early-summer sloughs and along the meandering creeks. Sandhill cranes spread their great wings into the sky in the company of golden eagles.

Thousands of swallows built their nests on the steep walls of river bluffs and Badlands buttes. The meadow lark, as now, sang his glad song-- but he sang over prairies more fragrant with purple vetches and sweet roses. Canaries and bluebirds, seldom seen now, flitted about the orange-red lilies and sunflowers of lusty yellow.

* * * * * * * * * *

At Pembina, the fur trader in the fall of 1851 shipped to market: "4000 lynx, 7000 mink, up to 8000 martens." Early settlers continued the hunting and trapping, finding in furs a side income as they sought to "tame the prairies" into profitable farm land. Many a homesteader depended on wild fowl, particularly the prairie chicken, as a staple food during the first years on his claim.

The jack rabbit and the coyote werè the last to be hunted. Because the rabbits multiplied rapidly and damaged crops, farmers in the Thirties and Forties organized rabbit drives and shot as many as five hundred rabbits in a single drive. Since the coyote killed sheep and young cattle as well as poultry, farmers and ranchers waged war upon it. E.M. Canfield and his wife flew over the buttes and canyons of western North Dakota and shot coyotes by the hundreds.

In recent years we have come to realize that man brings harm to himself if he destroys wildlife. So we regulate hunting, fishing, and trapping to prevent the extermination of species. But today hunting is less of a threat to wildlife than is the way we

12 - Farmers gather for a rabbit hunt near Bentley in 1921.

use our land. Wildlife must have food, water, and shelter -- and the kind of space in which it can breed and care for young.

At present nearly three percent of North Dakota's 70,000 acres of land has been set aside for wildlife -- and for the sake of people, for in the end, we really manage our wildlife for people. This land occurs as national wildlife refuges, waterfowl production areas, state wildlife management areas, school lands and parks.

Actually, the private land owner is the key to maintaining abundant wildlife. The way he uses his land and the degree to which other citizens assist through conservation programs will dictate the future of wildlife in North Dakota.

The vast herds of buffalo are gone, along with the wolves and grizzly bear. But through proper management of private and public lands, the antelope, deer, foxes, rabbits, skunks, weasels -- and grouse, partridges, pheasants, waterfowl, and songbirds -- can thrive and benefit people.

11 - Wind Wagons

Most Dakota settlers came from countries or parts of the United States where there were mountains, ranges of high hills, plenty of trees, even woods. They homesteaded on the prairies where the wind swept unobstructed by hills or mountains, and no trees, groves or buildings gave even temporary shelter from the wind. When the prairie pioneers wrote back home, they often commented on the wind that seemed ever blowing.

In those early days when folks sat around campfires or sat twisting hay to feed a stove in a sodhouse, they chiefly amused themselves with talk. To spice up the talk a bit, one or another might tell a story, stretching the facts as much as he could, to test the gullibility of his listeners. And now and then, some wag found satisfaction in spinning a tall tale that had little basis in fact.

One such tale told of a character known as Windwagon Smith. This red-haired sailor appeared on the prairies far to the south in Missouri. He had a strange conveyance of gigantic proportions. It had four large red wheels holding up a wagon box. Mounted on the wagon box was the deck of a ship with tall masts and great white sails. And at the captain's wheel stood Windwagon Smith in a blue sailor shirt and wide bell-bottom trousers.

As people came running to stare at this strange ship-wagon, Windwagon Smith called out, "Ahoy, mates!" and invited them to come aboard. His ship, he said, could take them out over the prairies to their claims faster than any covered wagon. As soon as he unfurled his sails, the wind would take them westward to the land they wanted to settle.

Legend relates that eager settlers crowded aboard the ship-wagon with their belongings. Then a strong east wind filled the sails and Smith's windwagon raced over the Missouri prairies. It flew past covered wagons drawn by oxen.

When Windwagon Smith spotted an Indian camp ahead, he guided his wagon-ship over a high hill so that it hopped right over the Indians. Then a tremendous herd of buffaloes came thundering over the prairies in a cloud of dust. But they didn't bother Windwagon Smith. He just lowered his sails and brought the windwagon to a stop. He ordered his passengers below deck. Then he let down a gangplank at either end of his ship-wagon so the buffaloes raced up one gangplank, ran across the deck and down the other gangplank and away across the prairies.

Well, on the Dakota prairies folks were not content just to listen to tall tales about the wind. A few enterprising folks decided they could harness that wind for actual transportation. An Eddy County man in 1899 raised the shafts on his buggy with rope lines; for power he used a house door to catch a strong wind and thus surged over the prairie for six miles. Some time later a Maxbass man fastened a large wooden panel behind his buggy seat and enjoyed a jaunty, though brief, wind-powered ride before he crashed.

Down Lisbon way in the year 1887, two young men, Thomas Oium and John Carlson, decided they could rig up a snow boat and beat the train to Fargo. They outfitted their snow boat with sails. They bundled themselves in buffalo overcoats and fur caps and huge fur mittens. Then on a day of high southwest wind, they hoisted the sail on their snow boat and skimmed off over the snow. Keeping that sailboat upright proved such a job they were soon perspiring despite the increasing cold.

Blizzard weather overtook them, and they could hardly see through the weaving walls of snow. Then suddenly they coasted right into a strawstack about two miles east of Tower City, and thus their flight ended quite off course. But judging by the time and distance traveled, they had made sixty miles an hour.

They spent the night at a farmhouse. The next day, with the direction of the wind changed, they decided to return home. No use trying to make Fargo. Again they traveled at considerable speed until snow again blinded them and a telegraph pole a mile north of Buttzville stopped them. They spent three days stormbound before they could continue home.

Yes, some folks put platforms on railway trucks, then raised sails and, powered by a favorable wind, made journeys between railway towns.

But the most successful of all windwagon operators was a priest, Father Genin. A French priest of the Society of Oblates of Mary, Father Genin worked forty years as a missionary among Indians in Canada. He established chapels at various places, started the first Catholic churches in Duluth and Moorhead, Minnesota, and in 1874 arrived at Bismarck to build a chapel there.

The following year, a Bismarck Negro, George Washington McNear, was frightened into confessing to a murder that he did not commit. Many people in Bismarck were convinced that McNear was innocent, but he had already been condemned to death by hanging.

The only way to save McNear from execution was to get a pardon from John L. Pennington, Governor of Dakota Territory. The capital was then at Yankton, and the telegraph line had not yet been completed to Bismarck.

The Northern Pacific Railroad had reached Bismarck in 1873, but the trains did not run out to Bismarck during the winter.

The compassionate Father Genin was determined to save McNear's life. A petition to the Governor was drawn up and signed by Bismarck pioneers.

Then Father Genin rigged up a sail on a railway handcar, wrapped himself up warmly, and pushed by a strong west wind, he raced over the tracks to Fargo. Here he telegraphed the petition to Governor Pennington who agreed to a commutation of the death sentence. And McNear was later set free.

12 - Wheat-Cleaner

As they drove past a settler's dugout, Ingbord almost shuddered. To live like a gopher in the ground -- no, that she could never abide. She was glad she would not have to write to her family back in Schleswig-Holstein and tell them she now lived in a dugout! Instead, she could tell them that her good husband Edwin had gone out before her on the Dakota prairie and built a house of lumber.

Long before their slow-moving wagon reached it that sixth day in April, 1879, Edwin Jensen pointed to a dark object on the horizon of grass and said, "There is our house!"

Already Ingbord knew she would love the prairie land. Everywhere the grass had begun to green above the brown earth and when they had halted to give the horses a rest, Edwin scampered about with their little boy, and Ingbord with the baby in her arms, found yellow and blue violets.

The 16 by 16 one-room shanty, Ingbord found, was indeed a simple home -- if one thought back to the comfortable and spacious house in which she had grown up. But Ingbord would not look back.

Their first morning in the shanty, Ingbord awakened to see two antelope looking into their window. Later, Edwin took his family to a nearby slough where great numbers of geese and ducks fed. Prairie chickens came close to the house, showing no fear as Ingbord walked among them.

How delightful this land where even rabbits sat up to watch Ingbord, their long ears twitching! Yes, the mosquitoes came in swarms from the sloughs, but Ingbord learned to keep a smudge smoking, and that kept the mosquitoes from bothering her as she dug holes in the ground and planted in them corn, cabbages, and melons.

While Edwin went out to plow fields for the new settlers coming into the neighborhood, Ingbord welcomed women less fortunate than she. Most of these homesteaders had no stove but did their cooking over an open fire or on a small heating stove that had no oven. Ingbord happily invited the women to bake bread in her small cook stove. So she seldom lacked for company as one woman or another brought her bread dough to Ingbord's house. And bachelor homesteaders came eagerly to buy loaves of bread from her.

To help him build a barn, Edwin hired two men. For the night each man brought armfuls of sweet-smelling hay and his bedding into the house and made his bed on the floor. In the morning, the men took out their hay and bedding so that Ingbord had room in which to cook breakfast.

During the first happy summer, Ingbord carried water from the Maple River; that fall she rejoiced over the luxury of a well dug near the house. And with fields plowed on their homestead, Ingbord and Edwin looked forward to the next year when they could plant their first crops of wheat. Surely ground that produced the large and beautiful ears of corn, the luscious melons and great cabbages they harvested that first year would bring them also a bountiful crop of grain.

Then tragedy came to the little family when the baby died. As the snows covered the prairie and the new little grave, Ingbord's heart ached, and she became homesick for the family and friends she had left behind in Germany. There was so little housework to do now while winter bound her inside with the boy who always reminded her of his brother. Edwin, too, grieving for the child, found work to do outside whenever the weather allowed.

That fall he had gone to Casselton where he had bought 50 bushels of seed wheat to plant the next spring. But at home he and Ingbord had found weed seeds mixed with the wheat. To sow the wheat the way it was, they would also be sowing weeds.

Now each day to keep herself busy, Ingbord took a white plate from her small cupboard and put on it a small amount of wheat. Then she picked out the weed seeds. Though she found this tiresome labor did not keep her mind free of sorrow and homesickness, Ingbord continued as the snow built larger and larger drifts about the house and hid the dugouts and sodhouses of neighbors. As she picked out the weed seeds, she tried to think of the grain that would grow from the cleaned wheat. She schooled herself to sing so that the little boy playing about her could believe his mother was happy.

Then on February 17, 1880, Edwin started across the prairie to find a midwife to come and help with the child soon to be born. He stopped at the nearest dugout and asked the neighbor woman there to stay with Ingbord. The moon shone brightly when Edwin reached the home of the elderly midwife and she quickly agreed to come with him. But on the homeward way, a blizzard struck and Edwin could see nothing through the shifting walls of snow. The strong wind hurled one of the buffalo robes off and away from the sleigh.

Edwin realized he could not go on. He turned his sleigh over. He wrapped the woman in the remaining buffalo robe and put her under the sleigh. He unhitched the horses. Then he drove them around and around the sleigh, stopping now and then to see if the woman was safe.

Early the next morning, the storm ceased and he saw his home scarce half a mile away. When he arrived there, he found Ingbord and the newborn baby well cared for by the neighbor. But he himself learned his hands and feet were frozen, and so -- with no doctor to treat them -- he put them in a tub of snow for a time. His feet and hands suffered no permanent injury.

Throughout the rest of that winter, when her family did not need her care, Ingbord busied herself with picking the weed seeds out of the wheat. But she did so with a lighter heart now that again she had a baby to love and hold in her arms.

That spring Edwin sowed the clean wheat over his virgin fields, and the harvest proved bountiful indeed. No more tragedy came to the Jensen family, and year after year because Ingbord had picked the cockel from their first seed wheat, the Jensens could sell their wheat at premium price for other farmers to sow.

13 - Overcomer

Inside a small white muslin tent, Eleanor Herrick lay with her six-month baby in her arms, and a child snuggled close on either side of her.

About the fragile tent the wind soughed through the grass. Almost before she heard it, she sensed the sound of an animal sniffing. It came closer. She heard the soft padding of feet nearing the tent. She froze in terror as the bright moonlight cast the shadow of a wolf against the thin tent wall.

As Eleanor Herrick prayed desperately, the wolf went around and around the tent, always sniffing. At times it stopped and pawed the ground along the tent wall. After what seemed like hours to the mother, the wolf left. Not until daylight began seeping over the eastern horizon did she fall asleep.

When her children awakened her that first morning in Dakota Territory, she wanted to run away from the tent and back to Minnesota. She crept out of the tent and saw the prairie stretching out for miles in every direction without a tree or a building for guidance and knew she could do nothing but stay where she was. Surely her husband would return the next day with lumber to roof the sodhouse they would build.

The sun shone brightly through the day as Eleanor cared for her children, doing what simple tasks were possible. Then toward evening heavy clouds appeared and strong winds began tugging at the muslin tent. During the night the rain poured down. It soaked through the tent roof, making their bedclothes sodden. Water pooled on the tent floor and the children clung shivering to their mother.

The next morning the sun shone warmly and Eleanor spread bedding and clothes to dry on the grass. From the little trunk she took out the last dry clothes for each to wear. This day her husband certainly would come and free her from her terror!

At noon they sighted him on the distant horizon. Though he was still some miles away, Eleanor and her children started in his direction. Through the tall grass they struggled. When they reached the wagon, they shouted with joy as they clambered on top of the lumber to ride back to the tent.

Quickly, Eleanor prepared a meal, eager to begin the building of their new home. With the oxen pulling the breaking plow, they cut strips of sod. They cut these into rectangular pieces, then began laying them brick-wise to form walls. For eight days they labored. And on the eighth day they moved into their new home -- four walls with one window of four panes, a door, and a roof overhead. The little sodhouse would keep them secure from rain -- and prowling wolves.

From the leftover lumber, they made three bedsteads. For mattresses, they filled ticks with sweet-smelling grass from a nearby slough. They looked out from the doorway of their new home and rejoiced. They had no money, but they had left Minnesota with debts paid from a failing business venture.

The land about them was stony. Since they lacked planks for building a stoneboat, they began clearing the land of stones by placing the stones in piles which they could later haul away. They managed to clear two acres of land and planted this to potatoes and rutabagas. Then they built a sod barn and cleared more land of stone.

In the fall they went to a woods two miles away and there gathered firewood. They gathered their harvest of seven bushels of potatoes -- and 25 bushels of rutabagas to feed their two oxen.

By January they had burned up all their firewood, and so they twisted prairie grass to burn along with buffalo chips they had gathered. By spring they had only bread and tea for food.

Then one day two men came from Fargo and filed on land nearby. They asked Mr. Herrick if they could hire him to break five acres of land on each claim. Glad for an opportunity to earn money, he happily agreed. Shortly after he drove to a settler thirty miles away who had a yoke of oxen to sell. Herrick mortgaged the oxen he already had and came home with the second yoke.

By fall the Herricks had redeemed the mortgage on the oxen, had harvested 900 bushels of rutabagas for their four oxen as well as a good supply of potatoes and vegetables for themselves. But again they were without money.

Then a government doctor from the nearby Indian reservation filed on a homestead a short distance away. Could the Herricks plow up thirty acres on his land and complete it before the ground froze? If they could do this, the doctor would pay them $60.

Since they now had two plows, Eleanor handled the second plow, following behind her husband. Day after day the two of them struggled to turn over the stubborn sod and on the fourteenth day of November the thirty acres lay black. The next day the first snow came in a furious blizzard.

Snug in their sodhouse, the Herricks felt triumphantly happy. This winter they had food enough to last them through the winter -- and there would be sixty dollars in cash from the doctor! Let the wind blow and the snow drift!

14 - Sodbusting Sisters

In the summer of 1881, three young people set out from Fargo, Dakota Territory, to find a homestead for each. Two sisters, Bertha and Anna Bergen, drove three yoke of oxen pulling a covered wagon heavily loaded with household goods and farm implements. Their brother, Christ, and a hired man, Magnus Olson, herded sixteen cows along behind the wagon.

They headed southwestward over the trackless prairies, wanting to find free land near the James River. In the sand hills area, such swarms of mosquitoes attacked the cattle that the cows went wild, and with tails in the air, bolted away from the men. The six oxen, fastened into their sturdy yokes could not stampede with the cows. And to protect the oxen from the mosquitoes, Bertha and Anna covered the beasts with blankets.

They drove the wagon to higher ground where strong breezes kept the mosquitoes away. Here they camped while Christ and Magnus searched for the runaway cows. A day later the weary men returned with all but two of the animals. (Not until two years later would they find the missing cows.)

They continued their slow way and reached Lisbon. Here they purchased lumber for roofs and loaded this on to their already large load. But they reached homestead sites still available near the James River.

Immediately, the two men set to work to make a barn to shelter the cows. They excavated into a hillside, then with a yoke of oxen hitched to a stoneboat they gathered rocks for building the front wall.

The sisters employed their own spades and dug into a nearby hill to make a dwelling, for in September winter's cold and snow would soon come upon them. Sixteen feet square Anna and Bertha made their new home and, with some occasional help from the men, sawed and hammered together a front wall of lumber into which they set a door and two windows. Over it they constructed a roof of lumber which must be covered with grassy sod.

The young women hitched a yoke of oxen to the plow their brother had purchased. Anna handled the plow while Bertha goaded the oxen and straightway they plowed up enough sod to cover both the roof of the barn and of the dwelling.

During the two weeks in which they built the dugout dwelling, they cooked their meals on a stove outside. To get the right draft for a fire, they just turned the stove to suit the fancy of the wind. Ducks, geese, and prairie chickens abounded in the area, so with Christ's ready gun and the sisters' cooking skill, the four of them ate well.

By the time they could move into their hillside home, the girls' dresses had tattered from the rough labor. Anna and Bertha looked into the trunks packed with modish clothes from Christiania*, Norway, and knew such clothes would never do on a prairie claim. They put the finery back into the trunk, certain that better days would come when they could again dress in style.

The two sisters looked out over the 160 acres each would acquire and were happy to patch dresses until they could again reach Lisbon and buy practical clothes. They felt a thrill in having built a dwelling with their own hands and set to work plastering the inside walls with clay and lime; the lime turned the walls white.

The prairie grass had browned by the time Christ and his hired man had finished the barn. They cut the drying grass with scythes and stacked it alongside the barn. Before the hired man

---

* Now Oslo, Norway

returned to Fargo, the two men dug a well and drove to Ellendale for a load of coal to provide fuel for the winter. They unloaded the coal in the shelter of the ravine near the dugout house.

But the first blizzard filled the entire ravine with snow, hiding the coal supply. No matter how Christ shoveled in the deep snow, he could not find the coal. So he and his sisters twisted hay to provide fuel for their stove that winter.

During the snowbound months, Bertha and Anna spun and knitted. Afraid of the sudden storms and blizzards that swept over the prairies, the three feared setting out for Ellendale for supplies. By February they had only flour, salt pork, and some coffee. But in March the cows freshened, little calves gamboled in the barn, and the Bergens had more milk, cream, and butter than they could eat. Once more they could make milk and cream porridges such as their mother had taught them in Norway.

As soon as the ground thawed that spring, Anna and Bertha yoked the oxen to the plow. Anna learned to plow a straight furrow over her quarter section of land and on Bertha's claim; their brother broke sod on his own homestead. Day after day, with Bertha urging the oxen on and Anna firmly gripping the plow, they turned the sod, rejoicing in the broad acres of rich soil.

Then while their brother readied the fields for planting, the two sisters gathered buffalo bones, loading these into the wagon. They hauled the bleached bones to Ellendale where they sold the bones for ten dollars a ton.

As the law required, they now built separate shanties on each of their homesteads. And that first spring, their married sister, Christine, came with her husband and five children with the intention of homesteading on a nearby claim. They built a frame house on their homestead, but Christine, unlike her sisters, did not find homesteading to her liking. So about a year later, the family returned to the hotel they owned in Fargo, proving up their James River homestead by paying part for the land.

The abundance of the first crops on the Bergen claims amazed the brother and sisters. Shortly before the crops stood ready for harvest, a prairie fire came roaring across the prairies on the other side of the river. When it reached the river, the sparks from the fire flew across the stream and so threatened the Bergen shanties and crops. Sisters and brother dashed desperately about to slap with wet sacks wherever sparks landed and started fires. They saved their property.

With glad hearts they harvested a heavy yield of grain. Their garden yielded watermelons and squashes of great size. The carrots were so large, the sisters pried them out of the ground with a pick.

More settlers came-- among them a young man from Norway determined to marry Bertha. While these nearby homesteaders built their claim shanties, they found shelter in the dugout the sisters had made into their first American home. As the new shanties multiplied, homesteaders celebrated with parties and dances. The three Bergens with five other homesteaders built a church.

A young homesteader came riding a fine horse to the little church and thereafter courted Anna. And thus it was that eight years after their first sodbusting, the two sisters married, Bertha to become Mrs. Hand A. Nevramon and Anna, Mrs. P.G. Forsberg.

The sisters and their husbands eventually moved to Fargo where they followed successful business careers. The Forsbergs built an elegant four-story house which for many years was a private museum recommended by the Smithsonian Institution.

15 - To See A Tree

Wherever one looked, the sea of grass billowed in the wind. Not one tree or shrub stood above the grass that often grew hip high. Here and there the low roof of a sodhouse or a tar-papered shanty lifted above the grass and gave the eye a bit of land-mark.

Near each homesteader's house ten acres of land lay plowed, ready for seeding. That spring of 1881 a group of families from the state of New York dreamed that when the railroad came their way, they would start a town, and they would call it Yorktown.

But the railroad did not come their way. Instead it established depots on either side of the settlement -- at Fullerton and Clement.

The New Yorkers sowed their fields by hand, and at the Van Kleeck homestead the mother eagerly took out the flower seeds she had carried with her from New York. Along the outside of the Van Kleeck two-room shanty, the father had sodded up about four feet. On top of this sod wall, Mrs. Van Kleeck planted her moss rose seeds.

That summer and for summers after, the moss roses bedecked the top of the sod with a tapestry of bloom and homesteader women and children came for miles around to see the blossoming wall.

A joyful person finding beauty all about her, Mrs. Van Kleeck gathered bouquets of wild flower blooms to brighten her table. If wild geese settled nearby to feed at dawn, she awakened her children to watch the thousands of birds. When she caught sight of a herd of antelopes leaping gracefully over the prairie, ·she called to her children to come and see.

After living in the settlement for several years, Mrs. Van Kleeck decided to take the younger children of the settlement on a picnic. She would take them beyond the small fields and the wide stretches of prairie that bound their lives.

So one sunny morning, she hitched up a wagon and with thirteen children aboard or running happily behind, she set off for the James River several miles eastward.

When they reached a hill overlooking the river, they stopped to look at what some of the little ones had never seen before -- water shimmering between the wooded banks of the river. They unhitched the horses and tethered them near the wagon.

Then Mrs. Van Kleeck led the way, the children following. She headed for the closest tree, a boxelder growing near the top of the hill. A flock of blackbirds fluttered out of the tree as the children, talking excitedly, approached.

"Oh," exclaimed the littlest boy, "is that a tree?"

"Yes," said Mrs. Van Kleeck, "this is a tree. It is a boxelder tree."

The boy followed her under the spreading branches. "My," he said, "it's nice here. It's cool here under the boxelder tree! I wish Teacher could be with us and see this tree!"

"That's nice of you," said Mrs. Van Kleeck, "but your teacher has seen many trees. She came from Fargo and they have many trees growing there along the Red River."

"Oh," said the boy, "I'm glad she has seen trees." Then he added, proudly, "I am in first grade, and I have almost finished the Primer."

For a few minutes, the children crowded into the shade of the tree. "Now," said Mrs. Van Kleeck, "why don't we all make a collection of the different kinds of tree leaves we will see? Then we can take them home and press them inside books or newspapers."

And so each of them gathered leaves and blossoms while Mrs. Van Kleeck told them the name of each tree they saw. Three ash trees grew near the boxelder on the hillside. Wispy willows clung to the river bank.

Mrs. Van Kleeck surprised them all when she took a jack knife from the large picnic basket she carried and cut a slender willow twig and made from it a whistle. With the first grader blowing the whistle, they wound their way in among a cluster of poplar trees.

Then Mrs. Van Kleeck pointed happily to a maple tree. "Oh," she exclaimed, "my favorite kind of tree -- a maple! We had so many of them back East. I was hoping we'd find maples here in Dakota!"

She set her picnic basket down. "Time to have our picnic lunch. And what better place than under this beautiful maple tree!"

An hour later, they turned reluctant steps back to the wagon and horses. Dark clouds came scudding from the west. They had traveled scarce a mile homeward when the rain began spattering them. Crowded together in the wagon box, they made a canopy of blankets over their heads.

That canopy had soaked through when Mrs. Van Kleeck drove up to a settler's shanty. A man and woman quickly came out the door.

"May we come in?" Mrs. Van Kleeck called. "I have thirteen children in the wagon."

"Of course, of course," the man replied. "You go into the house with the Missus. I will take care of your horses. It looks like a real storm coming."

The gracious woman hustled the children into the house, telling Mrs. Van Kleeck, "Oh, this will be fun -- to have company! To have children in the house!"

The husband returned to the house, dripping wet. And the rain poured down until dark, making it impossible for Mrs. Van Kleeck and the children to continue on their way. In the evening, the settler went out with his milk pail and returned with it filled. "Yes," he told Mrs. Van Kleeck, "we have three cows, one just freshened."

"And I just baked bread this morning," said his wife. "So we will have milk and bread for supper. That is about all we have, but you are so welcome."

That night, the husband insisted that Mrs. Van Kleeck share the one bed with his wife. Then he lay down on the floor with the thirteen children, some of whom had already fallen asleep.

The next day dawned clear, and while the soggy ground made pulling the wagon harder for the horses, Mrs. Van Kleeck and her children reached home without further delay, but too late to get to school that Monday.

On Tuesday morning, his eyes shining, the first grader brought his bedraggled collection of leaves to the teacher and told her the big news, "Teacher, I saw trees!"

16 - Where Is Crary?

In May, 1884, Mrs. John H. Crary prepared to leave Massena, New York, to join her husband out in Dakota Territory. But her friends and relatives objected strongly to her going. Over and over they told Mrs. Crary:

"You are going to be terribly lonesome out there away from all your friends and family!"

"That's wild Indian territory. It won't be civilized out there."

"That Dakota Territory should be left to the buffaloes and Indians. That's no place for a nice lady like you!"

"How can your husband support you out there in that no-man's-land?"

To all such objections, Mrs. Crary answered, "My husband is out there, and I want to be with him, and our children want to be with their father. There's a town out there named after my husband. He has written to me and told me that he is the postmaster and that people come many miles to get their mail. And he is homesteading on land, and so he will get 160 acres of good land just by settling on it. He has been out there for nearly a year now, and it is time our family gets together again."

And so, paying no heed to what her good neighbors advised, Mrs. Crary and her two children boarded a train for Chicago. There she took a train for Saint Paul, then another for Grand Forks in Dakota Territory. From Grand Forks she continued on Jim Hill's new railway heading west for Devils Lake.

Finally, on a beautiful May day the train huffed to a stop when the conductor called out, "Crary! Crary!"

Mrs. Crary and her two children stepped off the train and saw not a building in sight. Only sky and prairie greeted her. And then her surprised husband appeared. He had not expected them for another week.

Just that morning he had torn down the little sodhouse in which he had lived. He had planned to use the roof lumber for the new house he would build for his family. A pile of lumber lay nearby.

Once the first joyous embraces were over, Mrs. Crary asked her husband, "Where is Crary?"

"Right here," her husband answered. "You are standing right in Crary!"

"But the post office. You told me people come for miles around to get their mail. Where is the post office?"

"Right over there in the wagon box."

"How can you have a post office in a wagon box?"

"Come," said Mr. Crary. "You will see." He took his wife and children to the wagon and showed them a wooden box he had partitioned off into mail slots. "That's my post office," he said. "And I am the postmaster."

"But where is our land?" Mrs. Crary wanted to know.

With a proud sweep of his hand, her husband exclaimed, "All of this -- 160 acres of fertile land. It's all going to be ours. I've got a small field plowed and seeded. Just wait until harvest, and you'll see that Dakota ground grows crops you could never grow in that used-up soil back East!"

About this time, two young men came walking up to the railway siding where mail and goods for "Crary" were dropped off the train. They helped Mr. Crary to build the framework of the one-room house that would become the first permanent building in the town of Crary, Dakota Territory.

By nightfall, that house had no walls, nor roof. So the Crarys fastened some quilts over one corner for a bit of privacy and lay down to sleep under the stars.

But in the middle of the night, clouds hid the stars and soon the rain came. Hastily, the Crary family gathered their bedding and ran for the lone boxcar that stood on the rail siding nearby.

The next day the sun shone warmly and Crary took his family to see the small field where green spears of wheat thrust upward. Mrs. Crary looked over the little field and the broad expanse of prairie, sniffed the sweet fragrance of wild flowers and declared, "I am going to like it here!"

Indeed, so many people came by train or by horse or oxen seeking shelter for a night or a meal, that the Crarys enlarged the 16 by 16 shack to serve as a hotel which they named The North Star. In a corner of that hotel, Postmaster Crary kept his first little post office.

Not long after, a livery stable and a blacksmith shop became part of Crary. And when a depot was added with the name Crary plainly visible, no one ever got off the train and asked, "Where is Crary?"

17 - Plank-Rider

The lonesome pastor and the fourteen-year-old boy looked up at the tall timber. Short lengths of poles nailed to the big timber made a ladder by which one could climb to the top. At the top of the timber a heavy cable stretched across the Missouri River to a second timber on the opposite shore. From that cable there dangled an 8-foot-long plank.

"You see that cable up there?" the pastor asked the boy.

"Yeah! What's it for?" the boy wanted to know.

"Well, when the river is open in the spring and summer and fall, the ferryboat has a rope fastened to that cable to help steer the ferryboat across the river. But now the ferry has stopped operating for the season."

The boy pointed to the plank. "What's that for?"

"That's what the mail carrier uses now when the ferry isn't operating and before the ice gets thick enough to cross it with a sleigh. The mail carrier on this side of the river crawls up those ladder-poles to the top and fastens the mail bag to the plank. Then the mail carrier on the other side pulls the plank across with that rope you see fastened to the plank."

"And you think that we can ride that plank across the river?" the boy asked.

"Yes, I think so. But if you're afraid to go, I won't ask you to. I'll take you back to that place where we left our horses, and then I'll come back here and ride across alone and get home to my wife. I know she is very lonesome."

"No," the boy replied, "I don't want to go back. I want to stay with you."

It was getting late that afternoon in the fall of 1908. The sun would soon slip behind the hills. Both man and boy shivered in the cold. The pastor picked up the box of groceries. "You wait here while I get this box fastened to the plank."

Then with the groceries under one arm, he slowly climbed up the tall timber. The boy watched intently as his friend fastened the box to the plank, then came back to the ground.

"How high is that plank above the river?" the boy asked.

"I've been told it's fifty feet or so, and I think that's right. Now you go up ahead of me, and I'll be right under you in case you should slip."

So the plucky boy started climbing and the pastor, tucking a small suitcase under one arm, followed directly after. At the top of the timber, the pastor held the plank steady as the boy carefully slid himself out upon it, seated himself with a leg dangling on either side of the plank. Then the man settled his suitcase and himself upon the swaying plank.

With no one to pull the plank across from the opposite side, the pastor reached up to the heavy cable three feet above the plank, and hand-over-hand started pulling the plank forward. Since the cable sagged toward the center, the pulleys that held the plank rolled easily. But once they reached the center, the second half of the crossing became more difficult because it was an uphill pull. Often, the pastor stopped to rest and just hold the plank in place.

Neither boy nor man cared to talk on that unsteady plank fifty feet above the river which was now partly coated with a thin layer of ice. Nor did they look down. All the way across the boy kept watching his friend, trusting him to get them safely across.

At length they reached the other timber and with a sigh of relief, the pastor fastened the plank to the timber. He reached for the suitcase, then carefully got onto the timber ladder. With one arm holding onto the timber and the other steadying the plank, he smiled at the boy, stiff with cold, and said, "Now come."

With each hand grasping a side of the plank, the boy slowly pulled himself toward the pastor. The pastor stepped down one rung of pole so the boy could step on to the top rung. Then boy and man crawled down to the ground.

"Now, I'll go back up and get the box of groceries," said the pastor. "You stomp around and fling your arms around yourself and that will help you get warm."

A few minutes later, the pastor came down the timber with his box of groceries and joined the boy. "Whee! We made it across!" the boy shouted. Happily, the two walked through the snow to a homesteader's cabin and there they borrowed a team of horses and a sled that took them safely to the pastor's homestead in McKenzie County.

While other men tried it, only this pastor, the Reverend Ingvald J. Buckneberg, and the boy, Ole Bakken, ever crossed over the big Missouri on that swaying plank.

18 - *Gas Buggies*

The new-fangled horseless carriages fascinated sixteen-year-old Clarence Cummings. He yearned to drive a vehicle that needed no horses in front to pull it. With an automobile there would be no barn to clean of manure, no horses to feed and water, nor to harness and hitch up. But neither he nor his father had the thousand dollars needed for the purchase of an automobile.

Back there in 1908 the sound of an automobile sputtering down a dirt road or street brought folks to their windows to stare at the oddity. Not all people shared Clarence Cummings' enthusiasm for the "gas buggies." Newspapers reported stories of automobiles frightening horses into runaways, injuring persons and damaging horse-drawn vehicles.

The North Dakota legislature passed laws setting 8 miles per hour as the speed limit on a city street, 15 miles in the country. (The Dickinson city council ordered that 5 miles an hour must be maintained when driving around a street corner.) The legislature also required that cars must have mufflers and be equipped with a bell or a horn to warn at fifteen rods their approach near a horse-drawn vehicle. Auto drivers must stop if a horse driver or rider so signaled. Courts held auto drivers liable for damages to any persons or property injured in an automobile-horse accident.

While some North Dakotans sold their buggy horses and replaced them with an automobile, others who had driven their automobiles distances in the country sold their benzine buggies and went back to driving or riding horses again. Muddy trails, particularly the gumbo of western areas, and the occasional need to ford a stream discouraged the use of automobiles.

Tires with inflated inner tubes wore out quickly and "blew out" frequently. Some cars had solid rubber tires which also proved unsatisfactory. A team of farm horses often pulled a disabled automobile to a town where the new business of auto mechanics made repairs. Sometimes a car had to be shipped back to the factory to be rebuilt.

None of the cars that Clarence Cummings saw in Carrington were enclosed or had tops. So lady passengers wore chiffon automobile veils and "dusters" as protection from road dust. Those first automobiles in North Dakota were made by more than a hundred and fifty different manufacturers, most of them long forgotten.

Hardware stores handled the first auto sales, and local newspapers reported every such purchase. *The Larimore Pioneer* once commented: "Automobiles are on the increase in North Dakota, and those towns possessing one or more seem to be rather inclined to consider themselves more swell than a few of the rest of us." While some editors poked fun at the horseless vehicles, other editors hailed the benzine buggies as signs of progress.

Doctors and land agents were the earliest to use automobiles for business purposes. At Fourth of July celebrations, every gas buggy owner in the community proudly drove his vehicle in the parade. Prizes were awarded for the automobiles most handsomely decorated. And literary societies debated whether the horseless carriage would "do away with the use of the horse"

Clarence learned that some men in North Dakota had built their own cars. He knew that a man at Devils Lake had made a roadster for himself, and it was well known that Samuel Holland at Park River was making automobiles to sell.

13 - Clarence Cummings and his gas buggy, 1908.

Always of an inventive mind and determined spirit, Clarence decided he would make his own auto buggy. He had already harnessed the wind to give power to his mother's sewing machine.

Wind power could work on a stationary implement such as the sewing machine, but it would be impractical for a vehicle. So Clarence obtained a 2-cycle gasoline engine, scrounged around for wheels and other parts, did some tinkering and one day brought Carrington folks to their windows and outside to stare in astonishment as he drove his self-propelled vehicle up and down streets.

The *Carrington Weekly Independent* of November 26, 1908, reported to area subscribers: "Clarence Cummings, the

14 - *Clarence Cummings and his "motor wind sleigh,"
a forerunner of the snowmobile, 1919.*

milkman, was doing the town Sunday in a homemade automobile. It appears to go all right and have an abundance of
power. Clarence expects, when he gets it thoroughly broken, to
show the fellows with store automobiles how to do high speed
work without exertion. The machine is rather an ingenious
contrivance for a boy to get out. It has a two-cycle engine and all
the equipment to make it move, all of which Clarence built."

A few years later Clarence applied his inventive mind to
creating a self-propelled vehicle that could cruise over the
snow. This forerunner of snowmobiles he called a "motor wind
sleigh." And in it, Clarence skimmed over the snow at thirty
miles an hour.

For his motor wind sleigh, Clarence mounted an automobile
chassis on sled runners. The autombile engine furnished power
to an airplane propellor installed in a steel frame built over the
front runners. Clarence manipulated his motor wind sleigh with
a regular steering wheel attached to a steering apparatus on the
rear runners. A large windshield directly behind the propellor
protected the driver.

The local newspaper reported Clarence Cummings' adventures with his latest invention: "While Clarence Cummings was
driving his wind sleigh at a lively clip, Monday evening, the
machine struck the soft dirt from the sewer excavation near the
J.J. Walton residence and came to grief. With Mr. Cummings at
the time of the accident was Rollin Goss who was taking his
initial ride in the machine.

"... Neither of the occupants were hurt in the smash-up which
is considered most fortunate as the machine was making better
than 30 miles an hour when it overturned.

"The owner has already ordered a new propeller and other
repairs for the machine and expects to be spinning over the snow
as fast as ever, within a few days."

While Clarence Cummings was perhaps the youngest of auto
builders, records show that at least 60 automobiles were built
by North Dakotans those early years. However, by 1911, when

15 - Earl Branick's homemade "hot rod," 1908.

*16 - Homemade automobile by William Jones, 1910,
near New England.*

17 - Early touring car. Lady passenger is wearing a "duster."

18 - Ole Fosholdt driving his first runabout.

*19 - Hauling water in the "jitney," Divide County.
No self-starter in those days!*

*20 - A Model T touring car stuck in the mud—a major stimulus
for road improvement!*

North Dakota passed its first auto licensing law, folks had decided it was better to buy than to make your own car. Of the 7,220 autos registered that year, only eight were home made.

Most of the registered cars were gasoline-powered; the rest were 14 steam cars and 6 electrics. Nearly all cars were open -- touring, runabouts, or roadsters. Twenty-two of the manufactured vehicles had high wheels with solid rubber tires.

As the gasoline-fueled automobiles proved themselves for long-distance travel, automobile tours became common. Four teenagers made the news when they drove a Moline-Dreadnaught Touring from Astoria, Illinois, across North Dakota to Red Lodge, Montana, in the summer of 1911. Since gasoline stations had not yet come into being, the four young people purchased their gasoline at grocery and hardware stores, paying 12 cents per gallon.

At Bismarck, they had to cross the Missouri River on a ferry; the ferryboat operator puzzled over what fee to charge them. All fees hitherto had been per horse and per person. Finally, he decided that 25 cents would be agreeable.

Three years later, North Dakota ranked fifth in the nation in automobiles per capita. *World Today,* a national magazine, in its December, 1907, issue, observed concerning North Dakota:

"There is so little amusement in the plains region -- the mountains and lakes are nearly a thousand miles away -- and motoring opens up a wide new field for pleasure. When one may drive thirty to fifty miles in an evening over dirt roads that are as smooth as asphalt, with prairie breezes blowing health and rest into one's cheeks, it is worthwhile."

Persons who have driven on dirt roads will hardly agree that dirt roads are "smooth as asphalt." Indeed, it was the automobile's difficulties in traveling over dirt roads that brought about the hard-surface highways North Dakotans now enjoy.

19 - The Rampaging Mouse

After days of sleet and rain, spring had finally come to the Mouse River country. Down below their barnyard the Evanson boys watched the rising waters. "Hey," young Hans exclaimed, "wouldn't it be fun to make a raft—and just float down the river to the Sandviks' farm!"

But scarcely had he spoken when they caught sight of a man riding pell-mell into the yard where Pa was busy in the granary, cleaning wheat seed with the fanning mill. The rider must have caught sight of Pa, for he reined in his horse in front of the open granary door.

"Hey, mister," the man yelled, "the Canada water is on a rampage and we'll get flooded. They say this is going to be a bad one. Get everything to higher ground! I got to keep riding to the next three farms and get somebody else to take the message farther down river." And without another word, he galloped on his way.

"Hey, boys!" Pa called. "Get a move on! The river is going to flood—bad! Hans, you tell Ma and the girls. We got to move quick. Helmer, you chase the cattle up over the hills to the west end of the pasture. Ivar, hitch the team to the wagon."

Then to make sure that Hans properly aroused the women folk, Pa ran to the house. "Guri," he said to his wife, "the man said this would be a bad flood."

"Who was the man?" his wife wanted to know.

"Think it was that Irishman that just moved in where that German family left. No time to talk. All the furniture has to go upstairs. We got to catch the chickens and keep them some-where the coyotes can't get them."

"But where can we go—where stay—"

"Woman, right now, I do not know—but we got to get out of here!"

Pa turned to his daughters, "Take the chairs and tables upstairs. Just move everything you can move—upstairs."

Sixteen-year-old Astrid stared out the window. "Look! The river is already up to the pig yard!"

The sight of the quickly-rising waters sent the family racing to follow Pa's orders. The two daughters had gotten most of the furniture into the upstairs bedroom when they heard their mother exclaim, "The schoolhouse! We can move to the schoolhouse."

And Guri Evanson emptied her cupboard and her pantry into boxes and sacks, putting these out on the porch. And as Pa came rushing by she yelled, "Sivert, we can stay in the school-house."

"Good thinking, woman!" he yelled back and fled after a big sow that had escaped from the pig pen. Suddenly from the barnyard came the squealing of the first little pig the boys had caught. Hearing her baby squealing, the sow turned abruptly and headed back to the barnyard.

Pa found a crate which he lugged into the wagon. "Put the little pigs in the crate, Hans," he ordered, "and the sow will follow!"

Somehow in the pandemonium that followed, the Evanson family succeeded in getting the livestock to higher ground, the chickens caught and popped into gunny sacks. With the wagon loaded with sacks of seed wheat and oats, the crate of squealing pigs and the sacks of chickens and the sow grunting and following behind, Pa drove to the top of the hill overlooking the farmstead. Here he and the boys unloaded everything and returned to the house.

One look into the wagonbox, stinking now with chicken and pig manure, Guri suddenly revolted. "I am not putting anything from the house into that mess!" she announced.

For answer, Pa yelled, "Ivar, get a bucket of water and Astrid bring a broom." There followed a quick sloshing of water over the wagonbox floor and Guri, mollified, allowed the wagonbox floor to be covered with hay, then piled with her boxes and sacks of groceries, dishes, pots, and pans. While Pa drove the loaded wagon, Guri and her daughters walked along. The boys had been dispatched to see if they could catch a couple hens that had skittered from them into bushes along the river.

As they came in sight of the schoolhouse, Pa called out, "Guri, seems like somebody else had a good idea!"

And indeed the wagons and teams of three other families stood about the schoolhouse when the Evenson family approached. Small children watched over by older sisters ran about, playing some sort of tag. From inside the schoolhouse came the squalling of babies and the sound of many excited voices.

Out the door came Julia Swanson, Astrid's best friend, exclaiming, "You, too?" And so there were to be quickly seen some of each of the Swanson, the Lund, and the Berg families. And also quickly recognized was the fact that the small one-room schoolhouse could not possibly provide sleeping room for four families.

The one room would have to be used for cooking. The Lunds had brought along one of those new-fangled kerosene cook-stoves that had an oven, so baking would be possible if the Mouse River kept them from their homes any length of time.

"Sivert," said Guri, "we are going to have to sleep some-where outside."

"In the wagonbox," Pa answered, grinning slyly.

"Then you will have to wash it again. And get more hay in the bottom. It's too narrow for a mattress."

So off the Evansons drove, back to the farmstead where the waters of the Mouse now lapped into the barn. The boys had caught the vagrant hens and tied them into sacks, but when Ivar was about to toss the sacks of hens into the wagon, Guri objected. "No more chicken smell in the wagon! We are going to have to sleep in the wagon. The Swansons and the Lunds and the Bergs are staying at the schoolhouse, too."

"Ivar," said Pa, "there's a roll of poultry netting down by the chicken coop. Carry it to the top of the hill. And Hans and Helmer, you find some fence posts and staples and bring along all the tools you can round up. We got to fix a pen up by the schoolhouse to keep our hens in."

When the Evansons returned to the schoolhouse, another wagon drove up, a small woman driving the team. Two small girls sat beside her on the spring seat. The woman smiled and greeted them cheerily in English, "How do you do. I am Mrs. O'Brien and these are my little girls, Kathleen and Maria."

"Pleased to meet you," Pa replied. In his family and in the neighborhood of Norwegian settlers, it had always been comfortable to continue speaking in the language of their native country. He and Guri spoke to one another and to their children in Norwegian, but each of the children after a few years in school answered their parents in English.

Guri flushed. She had never seen an Irish person before. She had never talked to anyone but Norwegians. Speaking English was even more difficult for her than it was for her husband. But she managed a flustered, "Please to meet you, too."

Then Pa said, "I am Sivert Evanson. This is my wife, Guri."

Mrs. O'Brien looked toward the small schoolhouse. "It seems there is not room—for all of us. I—did not know—"

"We just make room," said Pa. "We all sleep outside that can. You have tent—or canvas over wagon?"

Mrs. O'Brien brightened. "Yes, we have a tent—if only Patrick will think to bring it."

"We unload your stuff in the schoolhouse," said Pa. "Then you drive back. Get tent."

And so it was. Little did the five families realize they must share the schoolhouse for the next four days while the Mouse River surged and finally crested. Fortunately, no rain fell for two days. But on the third, a constant drizzle kept all the women and children crowded inside the schoolhouse while the men and boys huddled on the ground under wagons.

The hens had scant shelter in the little pens where their owners quartered them, and yet they laid eggs. Each farmer went morning and evening (a few rowing in boats) to his own pasture to milk the cows, to care for any newborn calf.

And the Norwegians, speaking in halting English, found the Irish family much to their liking. And when the sun came out on the fifth day, Patrick played Irish tunes on his fiddle while the Norwegians danced about the schoolhouse playground.

Then on the fifth day, all could return to their homes. Yes, there was mud to clean out and brush and tree limbs caught against fences and buildings. And quickly the farmers seeded their crops, for it was late in the season that year of the rampaging Mouse.

Bountiful crops they harvested that autumn, and for many years to come these five families of homesteaders chuckled over their four days together in the little schoolhouse on the hill. And there it was that the Norwegian Guri Evanson discovered in Irish Mrs. O'Brien a friend she would cherish all her life.

20 - Sculptor

Out on the homestead claim near Wilton, North Dakota, a young boy busied himself with clay. Those first years, Paul Fjelde made rather clumsy-looking figures while he remembered the wonderful statues his sculptor father had made.

The family had lived in Minneapolis while the father, Jacob Fjelde, lived, and Mama Fjelde often had taken Paul to see his famous father's art. There was the statue of Ole Bull, the Norwegian violinist, in Loring Park; the Henrik Ibsen bust in Saint Paul; the bas-relief over the door of the University of Minnesota library; and near the waterfall in Minnehaha Park, Hiawatha carrying Minnehaha "over the wild and rushing waters."

On the farm, Paul's sisters sat as his models while he fashioned their likenesses in clay. One day while a neighbor lady visited with his mother and told of her husband's illness, Paul began to work industriously upon a lump of clay.

The neighbor lady, Mrs. Kuehl, watched him with interest. Paul's skillful fingers carved a small bust which he gave to the neighbor, saying with a sparkle in his eyes, "Here, you take that home to Mr. Kuehl. That's the doctor that I carved. Mr. Kuehl is bound to get well if you just keep the doctor around all the time."

Mr. Kuehl did get well and always joked that it was Paul's "doctor" that had healed him. That little clay statue became a treasure in the Kuehl home long before its sculptor had become famous.

In 1907, Mrs. Fjelde and her children returned to Minneapolis after having "proved up" on their homestead. Paul entered the Minneapolis School of Fine Arts as an evening student. Two years later, the family moved back to the homestead with the purpose of developing it and selling it.

The dry years brought only crop failures, so they next moved to Valley City. Somehow or other, they would manage so that Paul's sisters could go to the normal school there.

Paul brought with him to Valley City a few pieces of sculpture. His loyal sisters insisted on showing some of these pieces to Miss Mary Deem, the college art instructor. This teacher saw at once that Paul's work showed talent.

To help him pay for college expenses, she found a job for him at a photographer's studio. Since he did not have a high school education, Paul enrolled as a special student. "In six months," Miss Deem declared, "Paul advanced so rapidly that I could not teach him more; all I could offer was sympathy and encouragement."

She wrote to Loredo Taft, the famous Chicago artist. Taft agreed to help Paul, so Paul arrived in Chicago in 1912 to remain as Taft's pupil for three years.

So gifted did Paul prove himself that Taft allowed the boy to work with him on the Fountain of Time which he created near the University of Chicago.

When Paul was twenty-one, L.B. Hanna, the governor of North Dakota, called on him. Several men came with the governor.

"We hear you are quite a sculptor, Paul," said the Governor.

Paul smiled, pleased at such recognition.

"We have just been down to the Gettysburg Cemetery for the Fiftieth Anniversary," said Governor Hanna. "We saw just the kind of statue we think the people of North Dakota would be proud to send to the people of Norway in honor of the Norwegian independence centennial."

Gettysburg Cemetery ... Paul remembered that his own father had done the monument erected there to honor the First Minnesota Regiment.

"Right where Lincoln made his famous Gettysburg Address, there's a bust of him. Now, Paul, we'd like to know if you can make a bust of Lincoln for us."

"I'd like to try," Paul replied, hardly able to believe that here was his opportunity for a state commission!

"All right, Paul," the Governor decided, "you make a model for us. We'll be back later to see if it will do."

His important callers gone, Paul got to work immediately. He simply must create something that would "do." His fingers quivered with eagerness as he began to prepare the clay.

Lincoln! He was the President that Paul's Norwegian father had early learned to love and respect after he had immigrated to America in 1887. Ever since Paul had heard of Lincoln, a deep admiration for the martyr President had grown in his heart. Now he must express that love and admiration in this cold lump of clay!

Paul had barely finished the model when the Governor and his companions returned. They looked quietly at Paul's bust of Abraham Lincoln.

Paul waited tensely.

Then the Governor turned, smiled at the art student, and announced, "It will do, Paul!"

The other committee members nodded their approval and Paul had earned his first commission.

Several months afterwards, forty thousand people gathered in Frogner Park, Christiania*, Norway, on July 4, 1914, to witness the unveiling of the North Dakota farm boy's sculpture of Abraham Lincoln. Every year since then, Norwegians have gathered about the Lincoln statue to celebrate the American Day of Independence.

---

* Now Oslo, Norway

21 - Copy of Paul Fjelde's Lincoln bust in the Valley City Public Library.

In Chicago, Paul continued to train under Loredo Taft, happy for the success of his first public monument but realizing, too, that he still had much to learn. At the age of twenty-four, he moved to New York City and established his own studio.

During his lifetime, Paul Fjelde created many sculptures in plaster, stone, and metal—monuments both in America and in Europe. In 1917 he presented a bronze copy of the famous Lincoln bust to the people of North Dakota, and it was mounted on a pedestal in the house chamber at the Capitol. Other Paul Fjelde sculptures in North Dakota include the Bjornson Memorial at Mayville and replicas of the famous Lincoln bust at Hillsboro and Valley City.

The boy by whose hands many notable works of art were created had every right to be discouraged and to cry out that he had no opportunity. Drought seared the fields of the North Dakota homestead and yielded no income to pay for art schools. Paul Fjelde had no real sculptor's tools, not even sculptor's clay those early years—only the "kindergarten" clay that his mother provided him. But his widowed mother sang over the dreariest tasks, and she never failed to encourage him, saying that some day he would succeed even more than his immigrant father.

21 - Cookcar Girl

The cookcar sat in the shelter of cottonwood and boxelder trees not far from the big farmhouse. Newly painted white, it measured about 16 feet long and ten feet wide. A stovepipe poked up from its rounded roof. There were two windows on each side. Steps led up to a door at one end and there a large woman stood sweeping out a flurry of dust and dirt.

Kate paused, that August day in 1923, suddenly frightened over what would be in store for her. Mr. Tolliver, the threshing rig owner, had told her, "Just go right on over to the cookcar and introduce yourself to Mrs. Jenkins. She knows you're coming, and she'll put you right to work. She's been cooking for us for six years, and she can really turn out the vittles. She can get a bit hot-tempered if things don't go right, but she knows her business and you'll learn from her."

The way Mrs. Jenkins wielded that broom, Kate wondered if the handle might break. Well, the job meant three dollars a day and the thirty-day threshing run that Mr. Tolliver expected could net her 90 dollars -- more than enough to buy her that sewing machine she wanted so much. Life back on her father's sheep ranch would not be so dreary once she had a sewing machine -- and she could make clothes that were in style so she wouldn't feel so gawky and country hickish when she got to town.

Determined, Kate headed straight for the cookcar. Mrs. Jenkins caught sight of her and put down her broom. "Hoddy," she said, "You be Kate Morgan?"

Kate smiled, put down her suitcase and held out her hand. "Yes, I am Kate. I am here to help you."

"Hope you're better than the gal I had last harvest," Mrs. Jenkins responded. "You just put your suitcase under one of them trees for now, get on your apron, and we'll get this here cookcar cleaned up. It's gotta be scrubbed from top to bottom before we start cookin' in it tomorrow."

Kate opened her suitcase, pulled out an apron and then set the suitcase away. As she started up the step into the cookcar, she said, "I've never been in a cookcar before."

"You be some city gal that don't know the meanin' of work?"

"No, I live on a sheep ranch and I'm used to hard work."

"Well, it's hard work and long days in this here cookcar, and if you ain't been in no cookcar before, I got some explainin' to do, and good thing you come off a ranch where you don't have those new-fangled electric fixin's city folks got because nuthin' is fancy in this here cookcar."

She drummed her fingers on top of a barrel just inside the door. "This is for flour, and that little barrel is for keepin' sugar. Them two long benches is for the men to sit on when they're in here to eat and, of course, you know they would have to eat off this table. Up on the wall there is the bed you and me fall into at night—just a spring and mattress we let down at night. Up front there is our stove and sometimes it cooks both the food and the cooks. You see the cupboards up on the wall yonder? Whenever we move, we turn them benches upside down and pack the dishes in them. Sometimes we gotta be cookin' and bakin' even when we're movin' from one farm to the other. Ain't no picnic!"

Mrs. Jenkins put her hands on her hips. "Well, when we're with the crew, the water man keeps a couple barrels filled with water right outside the door. But right now we don't have no barrels of water. So you take this bucket and scoot over to that windmill tank there and get us some wash water."

Kate fairly ran to the windmill tank, scooped her bucket full of water, and returned to the cookcar.

"Cold water ain't the best for washin', I know, but I ain't startin' no fire until we have this place clean. Of course, it'll get

*22 - In the doorway of the cookcar stands the cook who
fed all of these men.*

*23 - Two crew men eat their lunch sitting on the ground beside
the steam engine. Williams County, 1905.*

24 - Ole Ellefson's threshing rig on the move. Hitched back of the steam engine is the straw rack, then the separator, followed by the cookcar.

25 - An old-time steam threshing rig near Page.

dirty again and again what with all them men trompin' in and out three times a day."

For an hour, Kate and Mrs. Jenkins scrubbed the walls, the floor, the benches and table, and the cupboards. Then they carried from the Tolliver house, boxes of dishes and cooking ware. In late afternoon Mr. Tolliver drove his wagon close to the cookcar and unloaded sacks of flour, sugar, dried beans and tins of groceries.

"My wife says for you to come to the house for supper and after supper we'll move the cookcar out to our first job. Crew will be coming tonight, so you have breakfast ready for them 5:30 in the morning. Pete Johnson will be bringing you a supply of eggs, butter, milk, and cream, some meat and fresh vegetables right after we get the cookcar moved. You'll be getting paid starting with tomorrow." And with that, Tolliver clucked to his team and drove away.

Kate found supper in the big Tolliver kitchen a welcome change from the afternoon of labor, and she was heartened to hear Mrs. Jenkins tell the Tollivers, "Kate? I think she's gonna do alright."

But they had scarcely eaten when Tolliver hurried out to his barn and soon came out with four horses abreast. These he hitched to the front of the cookcar. Kate had no more than gotten her suitcase into the cookcar when it began moving out of the grove and down the road to the neighbor's field. Skillets, pots, and pans jingled and jangled as the springless vehicle rumbled along. With the benches upside down and packed with dishes, there was nothing on which to sit. She joined Mrs. Jenkins standing at the back door.

"What are we fixing for breakfast, Mrs. Jenkins?" Kate asked.

"Pancakes. I'll be pouring out the dough, and you'll be flipping pancakes like crazy to keep up with 27 men eatin' like they never seen a pancake before. And there'll be bacon strips and coffee. And we'll have to get started with baking powder biscuits and cookies for the forenoon lunch, and get the bread sponge going so we can have bread for dinner and afternoon lunch. Usually takes about 20 loaves of bread each day."

It was ten o'clock that night when Mrs. Jenkins unhooked the bed spring and mattress and readied the bed for sleep. Wearily, Kate undressed. Mrs. Jenkins flopped down upon the bed, the mattress sagging to one side under her heavy body. Kate crept into her side of the bed. She scarcely heard Mrs. Jenkins say "We gotta get that stove fired up by four o'clock" before she fell asleep.

When the alarm clock jangled at 3:45 in the morning, Kate sat up with a start. "There's some kindlin' wood right outside the door," announced Mrs. Jenkins. "Get some in and I got an old Savage catalog I can tear paper from for starting the fire. And there's a box of coal. Fill that hod and bring it in."

Mrs. Jenkins lit the kerosene lamps fastened to the wall with brackets. Kate stumbled outside where a full moon helped her find the wood and coal. In the morning chill, the first warmth from the stove felt good, but how would that stove heat feel at midday with the sun beating down on the thin roof?

Three dollars a day, three dollars a day, Kate reminded herself. A brand new sewing machine from Sears, Roebuck. Sewing patterns. Dress goods. New clothes. She would learn to make pretty clothes for herself.

"Fill the stove reservoir with water. We gotta have warm water for the men to wash up with. Hang these towels outside on them hooks on the wall where I put the wash bench. Before five-thirty we put a bucket of warm water on the bench and set out a couple bars of soap." Already Kate was discovering that when Mrs. Jenkins said "we" she generally intended Kate to do the chore, whatever it might be.

At five-thirty the first men began sitting around the table where Kate had set out heavy coffee mugs, glasses of water, plates and tableware. Hearty "Good mornings" greeted the cooks, and occasionally "Hi do, Mrs. Jenkins, you are back with us again. And who is this young lady?"

"Kate. Kate Morgan," Mrs. Jenkins would answer.

As for Kate, she was too busy flipping pancakes to be able to acknowledge the "Pleased to meet yous" of several men. She had no time to observe that here was a gathering not only of farm neighbors and their grown sons, but also transient harvest hands, even one with a southern drawl.

Mrs. Jenkins carried to the table the first large plate Kate had stacked high with pancakes. In the other hand, she carried a large pot of steaming coffee. Warmed tin cans of "log cabin" syrup and dishes of butter were already on the table. "Help yourselves, fellers," she ordered. "We don't have no tea party here." That done she slid a large plate of bacon onto the table. Then she stoked more coal into the stove. By this time, Kate found herself not only flipping pancakes but also pouring dough into the huge skillets. She wished there had been time for a bit of breakfast for herself before the men came, when she observed Mrs. Jenkins sipping coffee from a mug placed above the warming oven.

As soon as a man had finished breakfast, he left the cookcar and another would take his place at the table. But in less than half an hour, the men had gone.

"We gotta keep some pancakes warm. The straw monkey and the engineer have been out there getting the steam up in the engine since maybe three o'clock. They'll be dropping in once they got things ready and the bundle pitchers have gotten out into the fields. And the water man -- he'll be poppin' in, too. But now you get yourself a bite to eat and I'll get started on them biscuits and that bread sponge -- I been snitchin' on the bacon and the pancakes myself."

By nine in the morning, the breakfast dishes washed, Kate had buttered and jellied the baking powder biscuits, and packed them into a dishpan covered with a towel. Into the dishpan also went a large jar filled with freshly-baked cookies. The threshing rig had already moved to a farther field, so the water wagon man came for the lunch-- and a sack full of tin cups. "They don't like to drink out of them tin cups," said Mrs. Jenkins. "With coffee in them, those tin cups get so hot they could burn your lips. But out in the field you gotta send tin cups because it would be too easy to break our regular dishes."

By eleven o'clock twenty loaves of bread were baked and a large roast of beef simmered in the oven. Kate had peeled about fifty potatoes ready for boiling. With the noonday sun beating down on it, and the big cook stove constantly throwing out heat, the cookcar felt like an oven. Flies buzzed outside the screen door and every time Kate went outside to fetch water or wood or coal, she fluttered an old towel to chase away as many flies as she could.

When the steam engine whistle shrieked for the noon break, and dusty, sweaty men lined up by the wash-up bench, Kate had poured herself a large glass of milk to give herself strength. By twos and threes, the men entered the cookcar, and the screen door not closing quickly, the flies flew in. Huge platters of roast beef, pitchers of hot gravy, covered butter dishes, platters of sliced bread with a cloth spread over, dishes of steaming corn and green beans greeted the hungry men. Two large coffee pots stood on the table while a third one was readying on the stove.

The noon meal finally done, Kate washed the dishes while Mrs. Jenkins made pies for the evening supper, and baked more cookies for the afternoon lunch. Scarcely had the big dishpan of lunch been taken away when the engine whistle pierced the air. "Ah, that's the signal to move!" exclaimed Mrs. Jenkins. "Hurry outside and pack in the men's wash-up things, and then pack all the dishes into the benches."

Scurry as she did, Kate had barely gotten the dishes packed when the steam engine, pulling the big separator behind, came puffing alongside and ahead of the cookcar. With a skill that amazed her, Kate saw the engineer back his engine and the clumsy separator in front of the cookcar. The separator man hooked the cookcar behind the separator and then after short blasts from the whistle they were on their way.

Mrs. Jenkins stood with two large potholders in her hand, ready to grab the kettles of soup steaming on the stove. "Stick some more coal into the stove," she ordered Kate.

Sometimes the cookcar lurched into a rut, and though the skillets and pans hanging on the wall clattered and clanged,

Mrs. Jenkins kept the soup kettles from slipping off the stove. Kate thought to herself, "She sure is bossy, but she knows her business!"

Half an hour later, the cookcar came to rest in another farmer's field. The water wagon man set the barrels down outside the back door, then having filled them with water, he clucked to his horses and hurried off to bring water to the steam engine.

"When do we serve supper?" asked Kate.

"They'll work in the fields until about sunset. You can't waste daylight as long as the weather and the grain bundles are dry enough to thresh. But right now you'd better get yourself some warm water into that small tub there, and there's a scrubbin' board by the back door there and some laundry bar soap. Some of these dish towels are soiled and there are the towels for the men outside -- get them scrubbed clean."

"Where do I hang them to dry?" Kate asked, for about them was no bush or tree, only a dusty field.

"There are nails all around on the walls outside. Hang 'em the best you can."

So Kate scrubbed and hung up the towels. She wanted to slump down on the wash-up bench and just sit there for a long time, but there was still supper ... Vegetable beef soup was about ready; it would just need warming up. Well, she had better get at peeling those potatoes again!

At eleven that night, Kate practically fell into bed and dropped right off to sleep. Day followed day in the same toilsome pattern and nights of seldom more than five or six hours of rest. But as her skills increased, she found herself less tense. Too shy at first to respond to some joking remark from the crew, she gradually learned to laugh with them. A highlight of each day was young Pete Johnson's arrival with fresh farm produce, meat, and groceries from town. Without refrigeration or ample storage space, such groceries must be brought every day or so, and young Pete came smiling and laughing, a new joke or story to tell, and always polite. "His ma brang him up right," Mrs. Jenkins said. "He's a nice young feller, Kate!"

Eleven of the harvest hands had "ridden the rails" to find jobs with threshing rigs. The threshing done, they would hop another freight train to seek other work, or to return to their homes. Such men were not as shy as the young farm sons. Like Kate, the farm boys' lives were spent in daily work on their fathers' farms with perhaps an occasional trip to town.

After seven days of threshing, rain came and soaked the shocks of grain in the field. Threshing must wait until sun and wind had dried the shocks. The farmers and their sons went home, and Kate and Mrs. Jenkins had only the eleven transients to feed. Having no work to do, some would linger around the cookcar, wanting to chat -- and tease -- the cooks, particularly Kate. Mrs. Jenkins would tolerate this for a while, and then would tell them to "scoot."

For thirty-three days, Kate worked in that cookcar. Weary as she grew from lack of sleep, the work had become less tiring as she became accustomed to it. On the last day, when they packed all the dishes and utensils away, Mrs. Jenkins laid her big hand on Kate's shoulder and asked, "S'pose you could stand workin' again with me come next year? I know I ain't the nicest to be around."

Mrs. Jenkins wasn't in the habit of tossing compliments around, and what she had now said was a compliment of highest order. For answer, Kate nodded, then put her arms around the big woman.

Pete Johnson's wagon clattered up at just that moment. He had come to fetch the leftover groceries. As he put the last sack into the wagon, he flushed a bit as he said to Kate, "I know where your ranch is. About twenty miles straight across from our farm. S'pose I could ride over and see you some time?"

"Sure. I'd like that," said Kate.

Back in the cookcar, Mrs. Jenkins' eyes twinkled and she teased, "I heard that. Nice feller, that Pete."

Kate's heart soared. Back on the ranch with a brand new sewing machine from Sears, Roebuck, she'd sew up a frilly dress to wear when Pete came calling!

22 - Nurse Boy

Eleven-year-old Herlof Anderson listened quietly as his two uncles, Philip and Harry, told their story.

Before Harry that October, 1918, would join the Army, the two brothers decided to visit their brother, Carl, and his family in McKenzie County. So the two boarded the train at Fargo for the long ride across North Dakota to Williston.

Philip and Harry had not been on the train long before a soldier sat down with them. A friendly man, he had just come from Camp Custer. There, he told them, an epidemic of the dread Spanish Influenza had spread through the camp, and dozens of soldiers had died. He was happy to get back to North Dakota on a furlough and away from the contagious "flu."

At Williston, Herlof's father met Philip and Harry and brought them to his farm home.

The small house on the Anderson farm became more crowded than ever now that the two uncles had come. Herlof had two younger sisters and two younger brothers. And just a few weeks before, Herlof's aunt on a neighboring farm had died of typhoid fever, leaving two small children, 7 and 3 years of age. Herlof's mother had brought the two home to care for them until the grieving father could find a housekeeper. To help with the housework and care for the children, Astrid Anderson then had hired fourteen-year-old Inga Arends. So the four-room house held a total of twelve persons.

Shortly after his two brothers arrived, Carl Anderson fell ill. Finding that her husband had a high fever, Astrid quickly called Dr. P. O. C. Johnson at Watford City, 10 miles away.

Meanwhile, Philip and Harry started doing the barn chores, feeding the livestock and milking the cows. When the cattle broke out of the pasture, Harry went after them alone because Philip suddenly became sick. After Harry brought the cattle home and mended the fence, he returned to the house where Dr. Johnson was caring for Carl and Philip. Both, he said, had the dread flu. He looked at Harry's flushed face and said, "I want to take your temperature."

He found Harry's temperature to be 103 and ordered him directly to bed. Now Herlof became the only "man" to handle the outdoor chores.

But news spread fast over the rural telephone line and all the neighbors learned that the Carl Anderson family was quarantined for the flu. They also knew that thousands of Americans had already died of the Spanish Influenza for which there seemed to be no certain cure. Much as they wanted to help the Anderson family, they feared entering the house where one person after the other became ill. Only Herlof stayed well.

Every day Dr. Johnson brought grape juice and instructed Herlof how to mix this with water for the patients, and how to administer medicine. All patients must stay in bed and drink plenty of liquid. Since there was no bathroom in the house, Herlof must carry the commode out and empty it regularly. He must go down to the well and pump water for his eleven patients to drink. He carried in water to heat on the coal-burning stove. Hot water he needed for filling the hot water bottles and for washing dishes, and warm water to wash hands and faces. Herlof fetched coal from outside to fuel the heater day and night, for the house must not chill.

There was the livestock to feed and the cows to milk. But when Herlof went outside the day his uncles became sick he found a neighbor, Art Smesrud, at work in the barn.

*26 - Herlof Anderson (in dark suit) with his younger
brothers and sisters.*

"I will do the chores for you, Herlof," Mr. Smesrud told him. "You stay with your family. I will set the milk outside the door when I have finished. You wash the pails in hot water and you put them outside the door when I come to do the chores. I don't dare come inside your house for fear I might catch the flu germ."

Every day, some neighbor brought food and placed it a short distance from the house and Herlof brought it inside. But except for himself, few had any appetite. The littlest ones did not become as sick as the older ones and sometimes got out of bed to eat a few crackers with jelly.

Dr. Johnson came daily with grape juice or some soup, encouraged his patients to stay in bed, keep warm and clean, drink grape juice and water. And he helped Herlof carry out the commode.

After a week, Astrid Anderson felt better and insisted on getting up to help care for the little ones. Then a young neighbor, Margaret Walla, telephoned to offer to buy the Andersons any needed supplies in Watford City. Astrid wrote out a list of items on a sheet of paper, then put the paper into the warm oven to sterilize it. Margaret rode up to the house on her pony while Astrid stepped outside the door and handed her the paper which she held by a pair of scissors.

By now, Herlof, exhausted from the almost constant care of the sick, became ill. As he poured his father's medicine into a glass, he collapsed. For the next several days, he lay fever-tossed, but happy to see that one by one his patients could leave their beds.

What Herlof Anderson did for his family was done in many other homes, by both young and old, during the nationwide flu epidemic of 1918-1919. Thousands of Americans died from the scourge. In McKenzie County, Dr. Johnson strove constantly to minister to patients scattered far and wide. During March, 1918, he and his driver slept only two nights in bed. When at last the epidemic had spent itself, only two of Doc Johnson's patients had died of the Spanish Influenza.

23 - "Tree-Tops"

Florence Gunderson was nine years old when she saw her first airplane. "Some day," she promised herself, "I'll get in an airplane, and I'll go up above the tree tops where the birds are!"

In 1919 when she reached thirteen, she learned to drive an automobile -- and go fast. Within a few years she and her brother George built themselves a racing car from a second-hand automobile. Not many people owned automobiles at that time, and horses shied to the roadsides when these two young Gundersons zoomed over rural Moorhead and Fargo roads.

A fair then came to Fargo which had along a commercial airplane. For a fee, the pilot would take people for a ride in this airplane. Florence lacked money for the fare, but she distributed enough fair posters to earn herself a free ride in the flying machine. Somehow, she felt disappointed in the airplane ride and lost her interest in flying.

When Florence was a junior in the Moorhead High School, her parents moved to a farm in northern Minnesota. Florence quit school to go with them. But life on the farm did not prove exciting enough, so she returned to Fargo to work in a store. She did not enjoy that either. Then a dry cleaner hired her to drive a delivery truck. Getting behind a steering wheel suited her.

Then Charles Lindbergh in 1927 made his memorable non-stop flight across the Atlantic, and Florence (now Mrs. Klingensmith) once more became excited about flying. After E.M. Canfield, an early North Dakota flier, took her for a ride high above the trees, she wanted more than ever to learn to pilot a plane.

27 - Florence "Tree-Tops" Klingensmith

She took a ground course at the Hanson Aviation School in Fargo. Canfield gave her some training and on June 23, 1928, let her go, solo, in his plane. From then on Florence Klingensmith made flying her life.

Her flying friends now started calling her "Tree-Tops" and the name stuck.

Next, she wanted to make a parachute jump. She bought herself a parachute and Canfield took her up over Hector Airport outside of Fargo. She made her first jump from an altitude of 1700 feet. But as she descended, she swung back and forth considerably and was knocked unconscious when she hit the ground.

Two weeks later, though, Tree-Tops went to Brainerd, Minnesota, to make her second jump. This time she jumped successfully. On the following Fourth of July, she jumped twice at Bismarck.

With flying in her blood, she went to Moline, Illinois, and took a month's course in aviation. Returning to Fargo, she was determined to get herself a monoplane. She called on Fargo businessmen, telling them how she would advertise Fargo with an airplane -- if they would provide her with one. "I'll risk my neck," she would say, "if you'll risk your money."

Six men bought the plane which they named "Miss Fargo." On April 19, 1929, Tree-Tops brought the new monoplane to the Hector flying field.

She was North Dakota's first licensed woman flier and 23 years old when she performed the first flying stunt that brought her national attention.

By eight o'clock on the morning of April 19, 1930, cars lined the road for almost two miles near Hector Airport. Tree-Tops had promised an exhibition of looping-the-loop.

At 9:06 a.m. the "Miss Fargo" took off. At 9:18, Tree-Tops went into the first of 143 loops. One hour and 13 minutes later she landed the small plane, and a crowd of spectators trooped across the field to cheer the daring young woman flier.

Actually, Tree-Tops had set an unofficial world's record for women by besting -- by almost a hundred -- the 46 loops made by Mildred Kauffman of St. Louis, Missouri. Only a few months later, however, Laura Ingalls of New York became the champion when she turned her plane over 980 times.

Tree-Tops could not let that record go unchallenged. At Minneapolis on June 21, 1931, before a throng of 25,000 spectators, she looped her plane until she reached a total of 1,078 times. During that four and a half hours of flying, she had made four loops a minute -- and had come within 355 loops of the world's record set for men by Charles "Speed" Holman.

Following this, she did exhibition flying in air shows all over America. Many thousands thrilled to her daring and her skill in handling an airplane.

She competed in the international air races at Chicago and on Sunday, September 4, 1933, placed second in the women's 30-mile race.

The following day she was the only woman to enter the $10,000 Phillips competition. For this race she was to use a plane owned by a Jackson, Michigan, man -- a lightweight plane whose original motor had been replaced by one of double horsepower.

Tree-Tops had come 60 miles on her way in the 100-mile race and swung closer to the pylons than any of her competitors risked doing when the fabric ripped from a wing of her plane.

The grandstand's thousands of eyes now followed only one plane. They could tell that Tree-Tops frantically tried to find a place to land her crippled plane without endangering the crowds below her. She made her way at an altitude of about 300 feet to a vacant nursery field where the plane suddenly nose-dived as though its pilot had fainted and fallen against the stick.

It was instant death for Florence Klingensmith.

Her body was brought to Fargo where fellow fliers and hundreds of townsfolk paid her final tribute. She was buried at Oak Mound Cemetery near Moorhead.

Acknowledgements

Before a book comes complete between covers, other persons besides the author have contributed their efforts and skills. Thanks go especially to the following individuals and their particular kind of help.

Terri Andreen of the Alexandria Public Library obtained materials and information from other libraries.

James A. Davis, reference specialist at the State Historical Society of North Dakota, Heritage Center, sleuthed through microfilm copies of old newspapers.

Doris Sperling read through early computer copy and gave her reactions.

My wife Beverly not only read critically the computer copy but also helped with the proofreading.

The staff at Echo Printing provided their usual cordial help and support in the printing of the book.

During the early 1930's, Angela Boleyn interviewed elderly women and wrote of their pioneering experiences in a series of feature articles for the Fargo *Forum*. My stories (12, 13, 14, 15, and 16) are based on the Boleyn interviews.

Some experiences were common to a time and place and not unique to a specific individual. These (1, 19, 21) I have narrated in fictional form.

In this book I have fleshed out the bare facts with dialog and detail logical to the event, place, and time.

PHOTO CREDITS

Anderson, Herlof - 26

Cummings, Stephanie - 13, 14

Green, Sheldon - 4

Hartman, Mrs. W. O. - 27 (This photo was used for *Extraordinary North Dakotans* in 1954, then returned to the owner. Since it was unobtainable in 1989, we copied the photo in *Extraordinary North Dakotans.)*

Haynes Foundation Collection, Montana Historical Society - 9, 10

Smithsonian Institution - 1, 6

State Historical Society of North Dakota - 2, 3, 7, 8, 11, 12, 15, 16, 17, 18, 19, 20, 22, 23, 24, 25

U.S. National Park Service - 5

Valley City Public Library - 21

ROLFSRUD BOOKS CURRENTLY AVAILABLE

GOPHER TAILS FOR PAPA "A classic children's novel about pioneer life on the North Dakota prairie . . . The story written by one of North Dakota's best-loved authors originally appeared in 1951; it is just as pleasant today." —Larry Remele, editor, *North Dakota History*

"Well-written in a clear, fresh style, the book and its excellent illustrations give an accurate and delightful picture of life in a small Norwegian-American community. —*Gopher Historian,* Minnesota Historical Society.

"It's a book that should be shared and read aloud, for the enjoyment of both children and adults." —Dennis Dalman, *Echo-Press,* Alexandria, MN

"The charm of Rolfsrud's narrative has to do with his way of telling, his knowledge of the subject, his quiet humor." —Rodney Nelson, Fargo *Forum*
86 pages, paper, illustrated

THE TIGER-LILY YEARS "A charming story, the more charming because it is true. For anyone who grew up in the 20's, it is delightfully, poignantly nostalgic. It is a wonderfully warm account of family life in an era that was on the brink of so many significant social and economic changes." —Lily Glydenvand, editor, *Scope*

"For some among us, the warm experiences recounted will bring memories; for the youngsters, who will enjoy it thoroughly, it will be a picture of life unknown in this day, but great fun to share. This is a dear book from the touching gathering of tiger lilies for Papa's funeral, to the ingeniousness of Mama creating long pants for graduation." —Arvy Hanson, Brainerd *Daily Dispatch*
103 pages, paper. Copyright, 1975

INDIANS OF THE UPPER MIDWEST History, customs, and culture of the Native Americans of Minnesota, North Dakota, and South Dakota. Illustrated. Paper, 133 pages Copyright, 1971

STONE JOHNNY SCHOOL "Erling Rolfsrud has captured all the richness and charm of a one-room school as he experienced it during the Great Depression. Teachers, parents, and children can benefit from its insightful message." —Mark Baker, editor, *Echo-Press,* Alexandria, MN

Stone Johnny School is a delightful fictionalized memoir about rural school teaching. Using personal experience as his source, noted author, Erling Nicolai Rolfsrud, brings special fondness to this story." —Larry Remele, editor, *North Dakota History*
111 pages, paper, some photos. Copyright, 1983

CUTBANK GIRL The book takes a fictional Minnesota family to western North Dakota in 1908 to a homestead they inherit. Here the Millers who speak only English find themselves in a settlement of immigrant homesteaders who speak only Norwegian. "Readers familiar with Erling Rolfsrud's books will instantly recognize *Cutbank Girl* as his. It carries the author's knowing marks of nostalgia and history, unwound in a sweet warm story. For those who don't recall the years Rolfsrud writes of, it's easy history. Facts slip by as well-documented details. Those who share the memories the author draws upon will relish its authenticity and loving treatment." —Kathy Friese, Fargo *Forum*

"In *Cutbank Girl*, Rolfsrud confirms the reasons for his popularity with young readers as well as adults ... It is the kind of story Rolfsrud tells best, combining a strong story line with historical background with emphasis on the good qualities of people." —Kathie Anderson, Grand Forks *Herald*
Paper, 117 pages, Copyright, 1985

SCANDINAVIAN MOSES
Biography of the late Knute Nelson, first Scandinavian immigrant elected governor of Minnesota and U.S. Senator. "*Scandinavian Moses* is a fine historical reader, written in lively prose that remains free of the often burdensome academic verbiage customary in historical texts. Not only does it stand as an important work for those of Scandinavian descent, but also for those with an interest in the infancy of Minnesota government." —Peter Kotz, *Carver County Herald*, Chaska, MN

Scandinavian Moses is no long, tedious discourse of an immigrant who succeeded. It holds your attention from the first page. To us, it's one of Rolfsrud's best." —Oliver Borlaug, *Leader*, Washburn, ND
Paper, 101 pages. Photos. Copyright, 1986

NOTABLE NORTH DAKOTANS
Stories about 24 memorable North Dakotans, past and present, illustrated with photos: Paul Broste, I.J. Buckneberg, John Burke, Anne Carlsen, Minnie D. Craig, John Christiansen, Marie Downing, Carl Ben Eielson, Fingar Enger, Agnes Kjorlie Geelan, Gudmundur Grimson, Fannie Mahood Heath, M.A. Johnson, Edwin F. Ladd, Grant Marsh, Harry F. McLean, Hazel Miner, Sondre Norheim, Fannie Dunn Quain, Vilhjalmur Stefansson, Dorothy Stickney, Victor H. Stickney, Era Bell Thompson, and Lawrence Welk.
Paper, 110 pages. Copyright, 1987

WITH THE WIND AT MY BACK
"*With the Wind at My Back* is a collection of 49 of the countless columns Rolfsrud has published ... The columns tell what it's like to live in North Dakota, from the teens to the present, from horse and buggy to spaceships, from barefoot boy to grandfatherhood. They concentrate on Rolfsrud and his family, but in a larger sense reflect life as it was and as it never can be again.

Rolfsrud was born to be a writer. His columns are short, the content is free of ten-dollar words and each article makes a point. There is humor, there is grief; there is elation, there is despair. But everywhere there is life as it was lived ... This is a book about a man with the enviable common sense to understand life while he lived it, and the enormous ability to tell others about it in good, solid North Dakota English." —Joe Dill, editor, Fargo *Forum*

"(Rolfsrud writes) not learned tomes on technical subjects or racy sex-filled fiction but warm and gentle tales spun out of the life of the pioneers, the sodbusters, life in the early years of the state, his experiences teaching school for many years and common, ordinary things like hanging clothes on a line but told in a way to tug at the nostalgic heartstrings of his readers."
—Carl O. Flagstad, Minot *Daily News*
Paper, 111 pages. Copyright, 1988

If your bookstore does not have these books, you may order directly from the author at Farwell, Minnesota 56327. (Telephone 612-283-5876) Except for *Indians of the Upper Midwest* which is priced at $2 per copy, the books cost $4.95 each. Minnesota and North Dakota residents must add sales tax. Schools and libraries are exempt from sales tax. For postage, add 90 cents for 1 or 2 books; 3-4 books, $1.25; 5-6 books, $1.60; 7-8 books, $1.95; 9-10 books, $2.30.